Study Guide for

SUPERVISION:
Managing for Results

SEVENTH EDITION ◄ ◄ ◄ ◄ ◄ ◄ ◄ ◄

Study Guide prepared by
GREGORY R. FOX
Vice Chancellor for Finance and Operations
University of Minnesota – Duluth

JOHN W. NEWSTROM
Professor of Human Resources Management
Department of Management Studies
University of Minnesota – Duluth

LESTER R. BITTEL
Professor of Management Emeritus
James Madison University

GLENCOE
McGraw-Hill

New York, New York   Columbus, Ohio   Mission Hills, California   Peoria, Illinois

Study Guide—SUPERVISION: Managing for Results

Printed in the United States of America

Send all inquiries to:
Glencoe/McGraw-Hill
936 Eastwind Drive
Westerville, Ohio 43081

ISBN 0-02-802492-3

1 2 3 4 5 6 7 8 9 10 DBH 01 00 99 98 97 96 95

Contents

HOW TO USE THIS STUDY GUIDE

This Study Guide is designed to complement and reinforce the seventh edition of *SUPERVISION: Managing for Results* in such a way as to enable you to

1. Proceed on your own in studying the fundamentals of supervision.
2. Relate supervisory performance to selected learning objectives.
3. Apply your knowledge of supervision.
4. Make relevant use of a variety of study aids.

The study aids used in this guide serve to

1. Reinforce what you have read in the text.
2. Provide a commentary on the self-appraisals presented in the text.
3. Check your knowledge of the material in the text.

Specifically these study aids include

Learning Objectives.   Before you begin studying each chapter, you or your instructor should establish exactly what level of achievement you wish to attain. In some instances, your objectives may aim at achieving an understanding of basic principles. In others, the objectives may aim at achieving an understanding of more specific points in making practical applications of your newly acquired knowledge.

Chapter Study Guide Outlines.   The systematically sequenced chapter outlines are designed to provide you with a programmed learning opportunity. Key words or phrases are frequently omitted from the outlines. You have the opportunity to immediately test your understanding of the text material in a comprehensive, organized manner by filling in the missing words or phrases. Keys to the Study Guide outlines are provided at the back of the book. However, you are advised to look at the keys only after you have made an attempt to recall the correct answer from memory. For those instances when that is not possible, work with the Study Guide and textbook to find the correct response. When you have completed this activity, you will have systematically completed an outline and notes for any given chapter. You can then make practical use of this tool for study reference as well as review preparation for tests.

Commentary on the Self-Appraisal From the Textbook.   Each chapter in the text has a self-appraisal exercise that gives you an opportunity to evaluate your aptitude and knowledge as a supervisor. Although each of these appraisals is scored in the textbook, the implications of that exercise are presented here. This gives you a better understanding of how the material in the self-appraisal relates to the material in each chapter of the text. This Study Guide, when combined with the textbook, gives you all the tools necessary to maximize your knowledge of the role of supervisors in today's modern organizations.

Self-Check of Your Progress.   The self-checks are designed to be self-administered; they should help you measure your grasp of the basic subject matter. Your goals should be to answer each question correctly and understand why the answer is correct. Each person learns in a different way and for different purposes. For that reason, the self-checks are divided into completion, true-false, and multiple choice sections. The answers to these questions can generally be found in the text of each chapter. The completion section frequently requires an understanding of the definition of key terms in the text. Answers may also be found in the Supervisory Word Power section following each chapter in the text. Keys to the self-checks are found in the back of this Study Guide.

CHAPTER 1 — The Supervisor's Role in Management

LEARNING OBJECTIVES

After studying this chapter, you should be able to

1. Identify the level of the supervisor's position on a management team.

2. Describe the major competencies that supervisors are expected to bring to their work.

3. Explain the linkage that supervisors provide between management goals and employee performance.

4. Discuss the resources that supervisors must manage and the results obtained from them.

5. Describe the different emphases placed upon technical, administrative, and human relations skills at various levels of management.

6. Discuss the need for balancing a concern for output and a concern for the people who perform the work.

CHAPTER STUDY GUIDE OUTLINES

Based on your study of the text chapter and/or your instructor's lesson presentation, complete the following outlines by supplying the correct answers for the numbered spaces. Some answers require more than one word to complete. Write the answers in the numbered answer column. Although you should rely principally on your recollection, you can use the textbook if you need help. Check your answers by referring to the key at the back of this study guide.

1 ▶ Members of a Unique Team

CONCEPT Supervisors are an essential part of the management team that gives an organization purpose and leadership.

Answers

1. __(1)__ is the process of obtaining, deploying, and utilizing a variety of essential resources in support of an organization's objectives.

1. _____

2. Managers plan, organize, direct, and control organizational resources. They direct the work of others rather than perform the work themselves.

3. Examples of managers include
   a. __(2)__ , who are in charge of other managers and establish broad plans, objectives, and general policies.
   b. __(3)__ , who are in charge of supervisors and plan, initiate, and implement programs intended to carry out objectives established by executives.
   c. __(4)__ , who are responsible for getting "hands-on-the-work employees" to carry out the plans and policies of management.
4. Some characteristics of the average supervisor include the following:
   a. The average supervisor is between 31 and 50 years of age; has worked for his or her current employer more than five years; has been a supervisor over five years; has been promoted from within the company.
   b. Seventy-five percent are male.
   c. Ten percent are nonwhite.
   d. Fifty percent work in white-collar settings.
   e. One-third manage unionized employees.
   f. Fifty percent are employed by large organizations.
   g. Seventy-eight percent supervise fewer than 20 employees.
   h. Sixty percent are first-level supervisors with no non-managers reporting to them.
   i. One-half of all supervisors make more than $35,000.
5. Several laws that impact on supervisory management are
   a. The __(5)__ of 1938 (Minimum Wage Law), which defined the supervisor as an executive who
      (1) Manages a department or subdivision; directs the work of two or more employees; has the authority to hire or fire employees; exercises discretionary powers; and spends __(6)__ of his or her work-hours on activities not related to managerial work.
      (2) Is paid a salary, and is not required to receive __(7)__ pay.
   b. The __(8)__ of 1947, which defined the supervisor as an individual who
      (1) Acts on the behalf of the employer "to hire, transfer, suspend, layoff, recall, promote, discharge, assign, reward, or discipline other employees, or [who has the] responsibility to direct them, or adjust their grievances, or effectively recommend such action," not merely in a routine or clerical nature but with the use of independent judgment.
      (2) Is prohibited from joining a __(9)__ .
      (3) May join a __(10)__ .

2. _____

3. _____

4. _____

5. _____

6. _____

7. _____

8. _____

9. _____

10. _____

2► *Many Competencies Required*

CONCEPT Supervisors must bring to their managerial work a broad range of technical and human relations competencies.

1. Typical professional and educational characteristics of supervisors:
   a. Three of four supervisors are promoted from within, with these characteristics:
      (1) Long service (they have held a variety of jobs).
      (2) Much more education than those they supervise.
      (3) The best and most experienced employees.
         (a) Knowledge of the job and skill are helpful.
         (b) It doesn't ensure that they have management skills.
   b. Of the supervisors that are not promoted from within:
      (1) Many are hired from __(11)__, or after completing company-sponsored training.   11. _____
      (2) Most are hired from __(12)__.   12. _____
2. Skills that help the new supervisor make a smoother transition to the management ranks:
   a. Place __(13)__ above all other job-related concerns.   13. _____
      (1) First concern should be about meeting quotas, quality, and cost standards.
      (2) Second concern should be about the __(14)__ who do the work.   14. _____
      (3) Last concern should be about __(15)__.   15. _____
   b. Successfully deal with the pressure from managers and employees.
      (1) Supervisors are the __(16)__ of the organizational arch.   16. _____
      (2) They don't throw their weight around.
      (3) They admit their need for help.
      (4) They come in on time and work all day.
      (5) They are physically prepared and mentally alert.
      (6) They abide by company rules and standards.
      (7) They cultivate a look of __(17)__.   17. _____

3► *Linking Goals and Efforts*

CONCEPT Supervisors provide the vital linkage between management goals and meaningful employee effort.

1. Responsibility to __(18)__.   18. _____
2. Responsibility to employees.
3. Responsibility to __(19)__.   19. _____
4. Responsibility to other supervisors.
5. Responsibility for __(20)__ with the union.   20. _____

4 ▶ Converting Resources Into Outputs

CONCEPT Supervisory performance is judged by how well supervisors manage their resources and by the results they get from them.

1. The major problems confronted by supervisors are
   a. Meeting operating and production schedules.
   b. Living up to prescribed standards of quality.
   c. __(21)__ .
   d. Maintaining cooperative attitudes with employees.

2. Supervisors must effectively manage the resources provided to them, including
   a. Facilities and equipment.
   b. __(22)__ .
   c. Materials and supplies.
   d. __(23)__ .
   e. Information.
   f. __(24)__ .

3. Supervisors are responsible for attaining
   a. Output or production standards.
   b. Quality or workmanship.
   c. __(25)__ .

4. The major job competencies required of supervisors are
   a. Technical know-how.
   b. Administrative skill.
   c. The ability to develop a plan to meet departmental goals.
   d. The ability to work with the manager to whom they report.
   e. Communication skills.
   f. The ability to deal with people inside and outside the reporting unit.
   g. The ability to deal effectively with people who report to the supervisor.

5. Table 1-1 in the text shows the list of skills needed for the successful supervisor.

21. _____

22. _____

23. _____

24. _____

25. _____

5 ▶ Skills to Be Developed

CONCEPT Supervisors strengthen their contribution to the management process by developing their technical, administrative, and human relations skills.

1. Supervisors perform the same management functions as all other managers:

a. __(26)__: setting goals and establishing plans and procedures to attain them.

26 _____

b. __(27)__: arranging jobs to be done to make them more effective.

27. _____

c. __(28)__: selecting and placing the right number of people in the most appropriate jobs.

28. _____

d. __(29)__: motivating, communicating, and leading.

29. _____

e. __(30)__: regulating the process, its outputs and quality, its costs, and the people who carry it out.

30. _____

2. All managers have many roles to play, requiring different types of skills:

a. Technical skills.

b. __(31)__.

31. _____

c. Human relations skills.

3. Emphasis among these three skills depends on one's __(32)__ level.

32. _____

▶6 ▶ A Concern for Both Work and People

CONCEPT   Effective supervisors balance the application of their skills between the work to be done and a concern for the people who perform this work.

1. Supervisory balance requires that as much attention be paid to __(33)__ matters as to technical and administrative ones.

33. _____

2. Employees who work for supervisors who are __(34)__ generally produce more.

34. _____

3. Supervisors must be prepared to handle __(35)__ problems a day.

35. _____

4. A method for planning a day's work is outlined in Appendix A in the text.

COMMENTARY ON SELF-APPRAISAL FROM THE TEXT

This exercise is intended to stimulate interest in the subject of supervision and to promote self-assessment. It is not a validated exercise, but its questions reflect generally accepted supervisory practices and attitudes. You may disagree with the preferred answers. If you do, support your answers by citing references in the text, especially those found under Concepts 2, 3, and 4 and in Table 1-1. It is important, too, not to take your score as a final judgment of your suitability for supervision. The purpose of the self-appraisal is to stimulate your interest in the field.

SELF-CHECK OF YOUR PROGRESS

Part A: COMPLETION An important term or phrase is needed to complete each of the following statements. Write the missing term in the space provided in the answer column.

Answers

1. Under the Fair Labor Standards Act, supervisors spend no more than ____ percent of their time doing the same kind of work as the people they direct.

1. _____

2. Most companies feel that supervisors are most valuable when they spend all their time ____.

2. _____

3. Betty has just been promoted to supervisor. She will have to make the transition to viewing ____ as her first consideration and as being more immediately important than other job factors.

3. _____

4. Kelly's department always has high output, but with considerable waste of labor, materials, and utilities, which are the ____ of the department.

4. _____

5. ____ is the principal measure of effectiveness in the use of energy and utilities.

5. _____

6. Quantity, quality, and cost are the main ways of measuring ____.

6. _____

7. Larry has expert knowledge of his company's production process and of the industry. These are examples of ____ skills.

7. _____

8. Mary is good at inspiring her employees and at solving problems that are interfering with getting the work done. Her ____ skills are weak, though, because she can't effectively use the company's information and records system or plan and control work.

8. _____

9. A(n) ____ is responsible for the performance of a group of managers.

9. _____

10. Since management is concerned with maintaining a continuous cycle from planning through control and back again, it is called a(n) ____.

10. _____

Part B: TRUE-FALSE By writing T or F in the space provided, indicate whether each statement is true or false.

Answers

1. Jason supervises a group of seven medical technicians who perform routine blood tests. He is prohibited by law from performing any blood tests himself.

1. ____

2. Under the Fair Labor Standards Act, supervisors are required to be paid under the same wage plan and given the same overtime benefits as the people they supervise.

2. ____

3. Most supervisors rise from the ranks of production workers, rather than being hired from outside as supervisory specialists.

3. ____

4. Many of the key personal characteristics of effective supervisors can be acquired or improved through supervisory training and development programs.

4. ____

5. The attainment of results is mainly measured through efficiency measures such as how well operating supplies are managed.

5. ____

6. The key words in measuring supervisory results are quantity, quality, and cost.

6. ____

7. The managerial functions of a supervisor are distinctly different from the managerial functions of a company's top executives.

7. ____

6   Chapter 1

8. Research has shown that supervisors who concentrate exclusively on technical job demands are sure to be the most effective.   8. ____

9. Gail is a white-collar supervisor; as a woman, she is in a distinct minority in this supervisory role.   9. ____

10. Supervisors perform exactly the same functions as all other managers.   10. ____

Part C: MULTIPLE CHOICE   Choose the response that best completes each statement. Write the letter of the response in the space provided.

1. A supervisor is
   a. The highest-level employee who isn't a manager.
   b. An operating-level employee with planning and scheduling duties.
   c. A manager.
   d. A production worker.   1. ____

2. Under the Taft-Hartley Act, supervisors are
   a. Permitted to join unions made up of production and clerical workers.
   b. Prohibited from joining any union.
   c. Permitted to join unions composed solely of supervisors.
   d. Required to be members of the same union as the people they supervise.   2. ____

3. Luis schedules the work of the other carpenters in his crew, but spends the great majority of his time doing carpentry work. Under the Fair Labor Standards Act, Luis is
   a. A manager.
   b. Not a supervisor.
   c. Not eligible for overtime pay.
   d. Not eligible to join a union.   3. ____

4. The transition from employee to supervisor requires a shift to
   a. Taking job duties seriously.
   b. Carefully planning the workday.
   c. Showing a concern for work quality.
   d. Putting organization goals before other job concerns.   4. ____

5. If necessary to protect some interest of her employees, Rose will readily ignore a company goal. In doing this, she is slighting her responsibilities to
   a. Management.
   b. Staff specialists.
   c. Employees.
   d. The union.   5. ____

6. For a manufacturer, raw materials are an example of
   a. Facilities.
   b. Resources.
   c. Output measures.
   d. Results.   6. ____

7. The effectiveness with which facilities and equipment are being used is measured by the extent to which they are kept working productively and by
   a. Whether workmanship standards are met.
   b. Whether they are protected from damage and abuse.
   c. The cost of the facilities.
   d. Whether standard procedures are being used.   7. ____

8. Typically, the most demanding skills of a supervisor are those related to
   a. Technical decisions.
   b. Administrative duties.
   c. Human relations.
   d. Operational planning.

8. ___

9. As a supervisor, Nathan is excellent at scheduling, work measurement, quality control, and the other administrative and technical aspects of the job. Yet the performance of the department is below standard. Nathan probably
   a. Needs to improve the supervisory balance.
   b. Could use better human relations skills.
   c. Is overemphasizing the task-centered skills.
   d. All of the above.

9. ___

10. In an AT&T study, the foremost job duty of an effective supervisor was found to be
    a. Attending meetings.
    b. Controlling the work.
    c. Training and developing subordinates.
    d. Managing personal time.

10. ___

<table>
<tr><td>CHAPTER</td><td>2</td><td>Coping With a Dynamic Environment</td></tr>
</table>

LEARNING OBJECTIVES

After studying this chapter, you should be able to

1. Distinguish between a supervisor's work environment and that of higher-level managers.

2. Identify the four characterizing features of work.

3. Discuss the general state of satisfaction that employees have with their jobs.

4. Explain how and why different people have different perceptions of the nature of, and the satisfaction they find in, their work.

5. List a number of ways by which supervisors can improve the quality of work life for their employees.

CHAPTER STUDY GUIDE OUTLINES

Based on your study of the text chapter and/or your instructor's lesson presentation, complete the following outlines by supplying the correct answers for the numbered spaces. Some answers require more than one word to complete. Write the answers in the numbered answer column. Although you should rely principally on your recollection, you can use the textbook if you need help. Check your answers by referring to the key at the back of this study guide.

▶ Seven Pressures to Cope With

CONCEPT   The unique environment in which supervisors work shapes their horizons and tends to restrict their options.

Answers

1. The supervisors' world differs from that of their superiors.
   a. They tend to be __(1)__ oriented.   1. _____
   b. They are less concerned with competition, creditors, suppliers, stockholders, and government regulation.
   c. They have the __(2)__ time horizon of all managers.   2. _____

2. The supervisors' environment is characterized by seven factors (see Figure 2-1 in the text):

   a. __(3)__, including processes, equipment, and know-how.

   b. __(4)__, including safety, health, equal opportunity, fair pay, privacy, and so forth.

   c. Organizational policies and procedures.

   d. Pressure from above to meet __(5)__.

   e. Competition with __(6)__ for scarce resources.

   f. The need to generate, process, maintain, and utilize __(7)__.

   g. The rising expectations of employees.

3. Changes in the future need to be planned for and may include

   a. Technological changes occurring more rapidly.

   b. __(8)__ of the business climate.

   c. A workforce that will include more __(9)__, immigrants, and middle-aged workers and fewer applicants with necessary skills.

   d. More emphasis on quality of work life.

   e. Economic uncertainty that requires quick organizational action.

3. _____

4. _____

5. _____

6. _____

7. _____

8. _____

9. _____

▶2 *The World of Work*

CONCEPT   The world of work is characterized by the necessity of employee conformity, the exercise of authority by managers, the subordination of personal interests to organizational goals, and the commanding presence of written records.

1. People work for these reasons:

   a. __(10)__ and the necessities and pleasures it will buy.

   b. The __(11)__ work can bring.

2. Weber identified four factors that make work unique. He called the system a __(12)__.

   a. Rules, regulations, and procedures are designed to demand a necessary __(13)__ in employee actions.

   b. A chain of authority makes each person __(14)__ to the boss, and the boss in turn responsible to another boss, and so forth.

   c. Managers are expected to place their interests __(15)__ those of the organization.

   d. Much of what happens or is expected to happen is put into __(16)__.

10. _____

11. _____

12. _____

13. _____

14. _____

15. _____

16. _____

▶3 *Employee Expectations*

CONCEPT   Despite its constraints, the great majority of employees are reasonably satisfied with their work.

1. About __(17)__ percent of workers are satisfied with their jobs.

17. _____

   a. Men and whites are most satisfied.

   b. White-collar workers are more satisfied than blue-collar workers.

   c. __(18)__ workers are more satisfied than __(19)__ workers.

18. _____

19. _____

   d. Job satisfaction peaked in the 1970s.

2. Workers prefer jobs that challenge their skills, make sense to them, and reward good work.

   a. One in __(20)__ don't do their best, in part because they feel that increased output will not benefit them.

20. _____

   b. Eight of ten workers say their jobs are __(21)__.

21. _____

   c. Supervisors can minimize these complaints by:

     (1) Living up to promises of promotions, and so forth.

     (2) Making sure employees have enough to do.

▶4 *Satisfaction and Dissatisfaction*

CONCEPT   Individuals have differing perceptions of their work and seek satisfaction from it in different ways.

1. Current employment is different from those of the past.

   a. Best educated workforce in history.

   b. We have legalized many __(22)__ such as equal opportunity, representation by unions, reasonable accommodations for disabilities, family leave, due process, and privacy.

22. _____

   c. Many employees expect and get __(23)__ work schedules, job sharing, and work-at-home privileges.

23. _____

   d. Employees are less certain that hard work, dedication, and perseverance will lead to job security or success.

2. Five factors influence the way people perceive their jobs:

   a. Past experience with similar work.

   b. Assumptions about the __(24)__ of coworkers or their boss.

24. _____

   c. __(25)__ about what will happen.

25. _____

   d. Reliability of __(26)__.

26. _____

   e. Present state of mind.

CONCEPT Supervisors can improve the quality of work life when they facilitate, rather than direct, the work of their employees and encourage feedback from them.

1. Two approaches to improve the quality of work life:
   a. Improve __(27)__ .
      (1) Buy the tools to make work easier.
      (2) Provide the time for employees to adapt to the task.
   b. Foster a greater involvement in __(28)__ .
2. Approaches to improve employee satisfaction:
   a. Offer opportunities for __(29)__ feedback.
   b. View many supervisory functions as facilitating rather than directing.
   c. Stay __(30)__ when and where you can.
   d. Try to be part of the total organization.

27. _____

28. _____

29. _____

30. _____

COMMENTARY ON SELF-APPRAISAL FROM THE TEXT

The intention of this self-appraisal is to help you understand some of the factors that affect job satisfaction. By looking at the problem through your own experience, you can transfer this knowledge to an understanding of the problem that supervisors must cope with. Don't be discouraged if your satisfaction scores turned out to be low. This is not a validated test, although it is based on generally accepted principles.

The statements can be classified according to the following categories:

The Job: 1, 2, 5, 7, 9, 10, 11, 12, 19, 20

Coworkers: 3, 6, 8

The Boss: 4, 13, 15, 16, 17

The Company: 14, 18

SELF-CHECK OF YOUR PROGRESS

Part A: COMPLETION An important term or phrase is needed to complete each of the following statements. Write the missing term in the space provided in the answer column.

Answers

1. ___ is a task or job in which a person applies mental or physical skills to earn a livelihood.
2. The two main reasons for working are ____ and satisfaction from the work itself.
3. Two characteristics of a(n) ____ are that it has a chain of authority and uses written records.
4. Most studies agree that job satisfaction is ____ among older workers than among younger people.
5. A reduction in the number of people employed by an organization as a result of unfavorable economic conditions is referred to as ____ .

1. _____

2. _____

3. _____

4. _____

5. _____

6. Alice usually helps her workers to perform well rather than emphasizing direct orders and instructions. She is ____ the work.

6. _____

7. Tedious, repetitious work in which employees can use little discretion or initiative typically produces ____.

7. _____

8. Changing worker attitudes have led many employees to place the burden of finding job satisfaction on ____.

8. _____

9. Civil and employment rights, such as the "right to equal employment opportunity," are often referred to as ____.

9. _____

10. John always encourages the employees he supervises to freely communicate any suggestions or dissatisfactions they have that are related to their work. John is encouraging ____.

10. _____

Part B: TRUE-FALSE   By writing T or F in the space provided, indicate whether each statement is true or false.

Answers

1. The only reason for people to work is that they need the money.

1. ____

2. The fact that Jerry tries to allow his employees to derive pleasure from their work makes him a typical modern-day supervisor.

2. ____

3. For the typical worker, the paycheck is relatively unimportant until other concerns, such as personal job satisfaction, are met.

3. ____

4. Studies show that, as a group, white-collar workers are less satisfied with their work than are factory workers.

4. ____

5. Marcia is certain that she does her very best at work nearly every day. The great majority of American workers share this conviction.

5. ____

6. There has been a distinct trend recently to increase the number of jobs that consist of only the simplest tasks with no need for decision making by the worker.

6. ____

7. Downsizing of many corporations has made it easier for employees to feel secure in their employment.

7. ____

8. Betty expects the office workers she supervises to be completely satisfied with their work. This is an unrealistic expectation.

8. ____

9. Encouraging free and open feedback from employees is almost certain to get the supervisor in trouble.

9. ____

10. Knowing thoroughly the real meaning of company policies and goals can help a supervisor make his or her employees' work more satisfying.

10. ____

Part C: MULTIPLE CHOICE   Choose the response that best completes each statement. Write the letter of the response in the space provided.

Answers

1. Which of the following terms is *not* necessarily associated with work, according to the view of typical modern supervisors?
   a. Lack of pleasure.
   b. Exertion.
   c. Physical or mental effort.
   d. Means of livelihood.

1. ____

2. What is the *first* thing a typical worker will look for in a job?
   a. Pleasant working companions.
   b. An adequate paycheck.
   c. Personal job satisfaction.
   d. Challenging and difficult work.

2. ____

3. David actively encourages employees to make constructive suggestions about improving work conditions and methods. This is likely to produce
   a. Fruitless complaining.
   b. A breakdown in the chain of authority.
   c. Greater job satisfaction.
   d. A workforce that ignores work rules.   3. ____
4. Rules, a chain of authority, giving organizational goals first place, and using written records are characteristics of what Max Weber called
   a. Private life.
   b. Group interaction.
   c. Bureaucracy.
   d. Informal organization.   4. ____
5. Of the following groups, which consistently finds the least job satisfaction at work?
   a. Male workers.
   b. Female workers.
   c. White workers.
   d. Black and other minority workers.   5. ____
6. Studies on worker satisfaction show that
   a. Most workers are reasonably satisfied with their work.
   b. Very few workers find any satisfaction in their work.
   c. Wages are the only factor that affects work satisfaction.
   d. Simple jobs are far more satisfying than challenging jobs.   6. ____
7. Jay always tries to see that his employees have plenty of work to do. This probably has the effect of
   a. Producing continuous complaining.
   b. Decreasing productivity.
   c. Interfering with product quality.
   d. Reducing the number of employee complaints.   7. ____
8. Most of the workers in Betty's assembly department complain often to each other that their jobs are boring and meaningless. Of the following, one step that would be most likely to help Betty improve the situation is to
   a. Give all the workers a 10 percent pay increase.
   b. Tell the employees that they had better concentrate on their work and stop complaining.
   c. Explain to each worker how his or her job contributes to the department and to the company.
   d. Increase the pace of the work noticeably.   8. ____
9. Supervisors who want to improve the quality of work life should consider all of the following except
   a. Develop a set of rules and stick to them without flexibility.
   b. Buy tools and materials that make the work easier.
   c. Offer opportunities for bottom-up feedback.
   d. Permit employees greater involvement in decision making.   9. ____
10. A supervisor can often make work more enjoyable for employees by
   a. Clearly directing every step in a task.
   b. Defining all directives in absolute terms, such as "always" and "never."
   c. Encouraging workers to complain among themselves if they wish as long as the complaints are never brought to the attention of the supervisor.
   d. Viewing much of the supervisory job as helping employees work effectively while allowing them some discretion.   10. ____

CHAPTER 3 Supervision and the Management Process

LEARNING OBJECTIVES

After studying this chapter, you should be able to

1. Identify the three most useful sources of generally accepted managerial expertise.

2. List the five functions of the management process and discuss how they involve a supervisor.

3. Given any of Fayol's management principles, explain its application.

4. Name the three most widely employed approaches to management practice and discuss the particular suitability of each.

5. Explain the value of contingency management in handling situations that occur in an organizational system.

CHAPTER STUDY GUIDE OUTLINES

Based on your study of the text chapter and/or your instructor's lesson presentation, complete the following outlines by supplying the correct answers for the numbered spaces. Some answers require more than one word to complete. Write the answers in the numbered answer column. Although you should rely principally on your recollection, you can use the textbook if you need help. Check your answers by referring to the key at the back of this study guide.

1 ▶ A Body of Knowledge From Which to Draw

CONCEPT Supervisors become active in the management process by applying established management principles and practices to operating problems.

Answers

1. Supervisors become managers by __(1)__ like managers. They
   a. Take a professional, disciplined approach to the working environment.
   b. Think in a __(2)__ way.
   c. Approach work positively.
   d. Accept responsibility for improving their organization.

1. _____

2. _____

e. Move from following orders to problem solving and decision making.

f. Understand their involvement in complex organizational activities.

2. Supervision can be improved by studying the five functions of the management process, the eleven basic management principles, and the three schools of management practice.

▶2 *The Management Process*

CONCEPT   The management process differentiates the work of managers from that of all others in an organization.

1. The management process consists of five functions (review Figure 3-1 in the text):

   a. __(3)__: setting goals and objectives and converting them into specific plans.

   3. _____

   b. __(4)__: lining up the available resources, designing the structure of the department, and dividing the work into jobs.

   4. _____

   c. __(5)__: (after deciding how many and what kind of employees a department needs) interviewing, selecting, and training the most suitable people for the open jobs.

   5. _____

   d. __(6)__: providing motivation, communications, and leadership.

   6. _____

   e. __(7)__: measuring results, comparing them with what was expected, making judgments of how important the differences are, and taking any necessary corrective action.

   7. _____

2. In theory, the functions are performed in order; in practice, the process may be shortcut or reordered to meet the needs of unique problem situations.

3. The purpose of the management process is to convert the __(8)__ available to a supervisor into a useful __(9)__ .

   8. _____

   9. _____

   a. The end result or output may be a product that is complete or partially complete.

   b. The end result may also be a __(10)__ provided directly to the consumer or another department.

   10. _____

   c. The end result should be at least as __(11)__ as the combined cost of the initial resources and the expense of operating the process. (See Figure 3-2 in the text.)

   11. _____

Name _____ Date _____

3▶ *Management Principles*

CONCEPT Management principles provide basic guidelines for supervisory decisions and actions.

1. Management principles can be thought of as universally applicable guidelines for carrying out the management process. They were first identified by Henri Fayol.
   a. Work should be divided so that each person performs a specialized portion. This is called __(12)__.

   12. _____

   b. Managers have the right to give orders and instructions, but must accept responsibility for having the work done right.
   c. Managers are responsible for discipline and morale, but must also be true to their word.
   d. An individual should have only one boss. This is called __(13)__.

   13. _____

   e. There should be one master plan or set of overriding goals. This is called __(14)__.

   14. _____

   f. All individuals, especially managers, must place their interests __(15)__ to those of the organization.

   15. _____

   g. Pay and rewards should reflect a person's efforts and contributions to the organization.
   h. Instructions should flow down a __(16)__ from the higher manager to the lower one.

   16. _____

   i. Employees should be treated equally and fairly. This is called equity.
   j. Managers should encourage __(17)__ among employees.

   17. _____

4▶ *Management Approaches (or Schools)*

CONCEPT Three widely accepted approaches to management practice have evolved, each with its particular suitability (see Table 3-1 in the text).

1. The __(18)__ approach.

   18. _____

   a. This approach relies on facts, accurate measurements, and analysis of the various work tasks and activities.
   b. It presumes that activities performed are best in a set order or path.
   c. A problem associated with this approach is that of expecting perfection.
2. The __(19)__ approach.

   19. _____

   a. This approach assumes that managers who understand human behavior get employees to willingly cooperate and produce to accomplish company goals.

b. It uses psychology and sociology of human behavior to understand why people act the way they do and to minimize conflict in the workplace.

c. Early proponents presumed if you followed the right directions and prescriptions, people would act the way you wanted them to.

d. Many authorities urge caution in applying a human relations approach.

  (1) Clear up __(20)__ problems first.

  (2) Let people try to solve their own problems.

  (3) Don't oversimplify the management tasks.

3. __(21)__ or situational management holds that supervisors and other managers must choose one or more of the three basic approaches (see Table 3-1) to fit the conditions that prevail in a particular __(22)__.

4. The __(23)__ approach.

a. This additional approach, with its interest in consensus and mutual goal setting between employees and managers, is similar to the human relations approach.

b. Employees feel committed to goals.

c. Employees tend to work with greater unity, requiring fewer controls and less supervision.

20. _____

21. _____

22. _____

23. _____

▶ Systems and Situations

CONCEPT Supervisors develop system and situational awareness in adapting theory to practice.

1. A system is a(n) __(24)__ set of elements functioning as a whole.

a. Each element is __(25)__ on the others.

b. Change in one part affects the functioning of the other parts.

c. Supervisors must not only manage their departmental system, but also must interact productively with other departments in the company system.

2. Supervisors utilizing a contingency or __(26)__ approach to management are prepared to use one or more of the management approaches depending on the situation.

a. First try the approach that fits your personality and talents best.

b. Double-check your results to see if another approach or combination of approaches should be used.

24. _____

25. _____

26. _____

COMMENTARY ON SELF-APPRAISAL FROM THE TEXT

The intent of this self-appraisal is to demonstrate the variety of techniques available to you as supervisors. Be advised that the management "schools" and their classifications overlap in both theory and practice. The classifications serve mainly to simplify the identification and recollection of the various concepts and techniques.

SELF-CHECK OF YOUR PROGRESS

Part A: COMPLETION   An important term or phrase is needed to complete each of the following statements. Write the missing term in the space provided in the answer column.

Answers

1. The end results that managers strive to produce from available resources are products and services that are usually called a department's ____.

1. _____

2. Betty tells people who ask about her work that the main part of her job is carrying out the ____, which consists of planning, organizing, staffing, activating, and controlling.

2. _____

3. The workforce, tools and equipment, materials, information, and similar inputs to production or operations are usually referred to as ____.

3. _____

4. John tells his boss, "The only way to handle that kind of scheduling is to apply advanced mathematics." John is suggesting the use of the ____ approach to management.

4. _____

5. The office manager uses his or her experience to judge whether he or she should be analytical in a given situation, or try to use human skills to increase understanding, or apply statistical and mathematical techniques. This manager is using the ____ approach.

5. _____

6. The Jones Company has a primary commitment to providing service of the highest quality. The dispatching department, however, consistently sets schedules to produce the lowest costs, even if customer service suffers. This company has lost unity of ____.

6. _____

7. Margaret takes orders from her supervisor and also directly from the supervisor's boss. Naturally, the orders sometimes conflict. This department has lost unity of ____.

7. _____

8. The formal channels in an organization that distribute authority from top to bottom are known as the ____.

8. _____

9. Joe believes that in nearly every circumstance work can be done more efficiently when a large job is broken down into smaller, specialized jobs. Joe is a supporter of ____.

9. _____

10. Lupe believes that each element of her job is interrelated and that a change in one element affects the functioning of the entire job. She has a ____ awareness of her job.

10. _____

Part B: TRUE-FALSE   By writing T or F in the space provided, indicate whether each statement is true or false.

Answers

1. The systematic approach is a good way to deal with process-oriented management problems.

1. ____

2. The Japanese management approach emphasizes consensus and mutual goal setting.

2. ____

3. Valerie's use of emotion during management discussions proves that she understands the disciplined approach to supervision.

3. ____

4. Joe, who supervises the maintenance crew, and Barbara, who manages the company's sales force, both carry out essentially the same management process.

4. ____

5. The management function of controlling relies mainly on issuing orders to employees.

5. ____

6. Clint is very careful to support and encourage the employees he supervises. In doing this he is protecting a resource of the department.

6. ____

7. It has become pretty clear in recent years that the quantitative approach is the best to use in nearly all management situations.

7. ____

8. When Bob makes careful measurements of the physical movements that the people in his department make while carrying out their jobs, he is applying the human relations approach to management.

8. ____

9. Carol, who works in the sorting room, reports directly to her supervisor, Martha. She is also fairly often given direct orders by Gary, who supervises the packing room. This situation violates Fayol's principle of unity of command.

9. ____

10. The true meaning of the contingency approach to management is that a supervisor should take no action unless a serious problem demands some response.

10. ____

Part C: MULTIPLE CHOICE   Choose the response that best completes each statement. Write the letter of the response in the space provided.

1. Joan is in the process of deciding which of the work tasks in the department will be assigned to individual jobs. She is

Answers

a. Activating.
b. Controlling.
c. Organizing.
d. Planning.

1. ____

2. Which of the following would most likely be a damaging violation of the principle of following the chain of command?
   a. A middle manager gives work orders directly to an employee, bypassing the employee's supervisor.
   b. A worker in the press room passes some information on a job directly to another employee in the bindery.
   c. An employee voices a complaint to his supervisor about a worker in another department.
   d. A middle manager tells an employee's supervisor that she doesn't think the employee's work is satisfactory.   2. ____

3. Of the following, which is a key word associated with activating?
   a. Leadership.
   b. Communication.
   c. Motivation.
   d. All of the above.   3. ____

4. The management process is
   a. Performed once each year.
   b. Carried on continuously throughout operations.
   c. Performed once each quarter.
   d. Only used when work conditions change, as when a new order arrives.   4. ____

5. Which of the following information would the top executive of a business not need to determine whether the company has made a profit on a particular unit of output?
   a. The price at which the unit is offered for sale.
   b. Which department produced the unit.
   c. The total cost of producing the unit.
   d. Whether the unit has been sold or not.   5. ____

6. The raw materials that go into a manufactured product can best be described as
   a. Resources.
   b. Waste.
   c. Output.
   d. Technology.   6. ____

7. Which of the following is most closely related to the goal of the human relations approach to management?
   a. Clear, precise work orders.
   b. Outstanding job design.
   c. Willing cooperation.
   d. Precise measurement of human skill factors in working.   7. ____

8. On one occasion, Larry uses careful, rational work scheduling; on another occasion, he concentrates on listening to the feelings of an employee; and on another occasion, he uses statistical analysis to find the source of quality failures. He is using
   a. The systematic approach.
   b. The human relations approach.
   c. The quantitative approach.
   d. The contingency approach.   8. ____

9. Generally speaking, the toughest problems a supervisor faces arise from
   a. Equipment failures.
   b. Company plans and procedures.
   c. Human beings.
   d. Inadequate resources for the job at hand.   9. ____

10. In a small furniture-manufacturing shop, one person cuts, another shapes, and others assemble and finish. This is an example of Fayol's principle of
   a. Unity of command.
   b. Division of work.
   c. Unity of direction.
   d. Chain of command.   10. ___

4 Making Plans and Carrying Out Policy

LEARNING OBJECTIVES

After studying this chapter, you should be able to

1. Differentiate among the various terms associated with the planning process.

2. Create a representative set of objectives for a department supervisor.

3. Explain the planning process and the differences between long- and short-range plans and between standing and single-use plans.

4. Discuss various guidelines for developing efficient departmental schedules.

5. Identify and explain the applications of the Gantt chart, the PERT chart, and the work-distribution chart.

6. Discuss a supervisor's responsibilities for interpreting and implementing a company's policies.

CHAPTER STUDY GUIDE OUTLINES

Based on your study of the text chapter and/or your instructor's lesson presentation, complete the following outlines by supplying the correct answers for the numbered spaces. Some answers require more than one word to complete. Write the answers in the numbered answer column. Although you should rely principally on your recollection, you can use the textbook if you need help. Check your answers by referring to the key at the back of this study guide.

1 ▶ Road Maps of an Organization

CONCEPT   Planning sets the goals and provides the road map for almost all of a supervisor's actions.

1. Supervisors play a key role in the planning process.

   a. Unless they accept this managerial responsibility, they will waste time, materials, supplies, __(1)__ , space, and __(2)__ .

   b. Supervisors are responsible for __(3)__ (tactical) plans, and higher executives are responsible for __(4)__ (strategic) plans. (See Figure 4-1 in the text.)

Answers

1. _____

2. _____

3. _____

4. _____

2. The planning process involves the following steps:
   a. Setting targets—goals, standards, or objectives.
   b. Setting guidelines to reach targets: __(5)__ .
   c. Establishing plans, which consist of
      (1) __(6)__ of what must be done including starting and finishing times.
      (2) Procedures, which prescribe the exact methods and sequences to be followed.
      (3) Rules and regulations establishing the limits (controls) within which employees are free to do the job their own way.

5. _____

6. _____

2 ▶ *Goal Setting*

CONCEPT   A supervisor's goals shape the targets toward which all of her or his plans and actions should be directed.

1. Goal setting for a supervisor involves seven steps. (See Table 4-1 in the text.)
   a. Consider the goals of the entire organization.
   b. Estimate the department's __(7)__ .
   c. Don't restrict your thinking at an early stage.
   d. Consult with those who will help carry out the work and others who can help.
   e. Pick a reasonable set of goals that contribute to organizational goals and are __(8)__ by the department.
   f. Place goals in a __(9)__ .
   g. Base plans on realistic planning premises.
2. A supervisor's goals are to
   a. Provide targets for the near future.
   b. Pin down departmental output, quality of workmanship, and allowable expenditures.
   c. Focus on departmental attendance, labor turnover, and safety.
3. A supervisor's goals are most often stated in quantitative terms.
4. Goals and objectives should include
   a. A statement of __(10)__ .
   b. Explicitly stated __(11)__ that are clear and measurable.
   c. Time orientation—output must be related to a time period.

7. _____

8. _____

9. _____

10. _____

11. _____

3 ▸ *The Planning Process*

CONCEPT   The planning process should be systematic, yet it should allow for flexibility.

1. Once goals are set, establish a __(12)__ to meet those goals.

   12. _____

   a. Develop a master plan focusing on the main objective.

   b. Draw up supporting plans that show how each activity can contribute to the master plan.

   c. Put numbers and dates on everything you can.

   d. Pin down assignments.

   e. __(13)__ the plan to all concerned.

   13. _____

   f. Review your plans regularly—be flexible enough to anticipate and allow for an alternative course of action.

2. Be aware of the different types of plans.

   a. Long-range plans—two to five years.

   b. Short-range plans—one year or less.

   c. __(14)__ plans—ongoing with little change from year to year; for example, employment practices and health and safety issues.

   14. _____

   d. __(15)__ plans—used once and they need revision; for example, department budgets and operating schedules.

   15. _____

3. Use a five-point planning chart to help check and control plans and keep them on track.

   a. *What* spells out objectives in terms of output, quality, and costs.

   b. *Where* sets the location for the assignment.

   c. *When* records the time estimates for the work.

   d. *How* verifies the methods, procedures, and job sequences.

   e. *Who* designates authority and control over resources.

4 ▸ *Scheduling Guidelines*

CONCEPT   Scheduling brings the planning process right down to the shop floor.

1. Make sure not to schedule employees at __(16)__ capacity because it doesn't permit time to handle emergencies.

   16. _____

2. To minimize the problem of employees stretching work to fill the time, plan a backlog of second-priority jobs to assign during slow periods.

3. Remember that __(17)__ occur when employees are assigned overtime; this results in a 5 to 10 percent drop in productivity.

17. _____

4. Resist the desire to promise what you can't deliver.

5▶ Methods and Techniques

> **CONCEPT** Supervisors may draw from a range of established planning and scheduling techniques.

1. A Gantt chart is a __(18)__ chart that schedules work to maximize the utilization of resources available to the supervisor. (See Figure 4-2 in the text.)

18. _____

   a. Requires rigid adherence to the operating sequence.
   b. Encourages overlapping orders and disregard for the sequence of orders received.

2. PERT (program evaluation and review technique) is a graphic technique that borrows from Gantt charts the idea of related tasks, ties them to critical events that are related to each other, and enables planners to identify __(19)__ in a schedule, plan, or program. (See Figure 4-3 in the text.)

19. _____

   a. Dramatizes the value of doing two or more things at the same time.
   b. Is most useful for __(20)__ projects.

20. _____

   c. Helps schedule a number of jobs to be done in a short period of time.

3. Office scheduling is based on the same considerations as production scheduling.
   a. Tasks to be done.
   b. Time to do each task.
   c. Number and qualifications of employees.
   d. Capacity and availability of machines and equipment. (See Table 4-2 in the text.)

6▶ Policies

> **CONCEPT** Policies provide the guidelines that help keep an entire organization working toward the same goals in the same way.

1. Policies are broad guidelines, philosophies, or principles that management establishes in support of its __(21)__ goals and that it must follow in seeking them.

21. _____

a. They are generally set by __(22)__ managers.

b. __(23)__ are needed to translate them into action.

c. Many policies may be unwritten.

d. Supervisors should __(24)__ change policy, but they should make their feelings known so they may influence change.

2. A supervisor's actions and company __(25)__ should appear as one and the same to an employee.

22. _____

23. _____

24. _____

25. _____

COMMENTARY ON SELF-APPRAISAL FROM THE TEXT

This self-appraisal is a straightforward matching exercise in terminology. A good grasp of the vocabulary of planning, plans, schedules, and policy is needed to fully understand not only a supervisor's planning responsibilities, but also those for controlling. As with all terminology for management and business, remember that you may encounter different terms—and different interpretations of these terms—depending on where you work.

SELF-CHECK OF YOUR PROGRESS

Part A: COMPLETION   An important term or phrase is needed to complete each of the following statements. Write the missing term in the space provided in the answer column.

Answers

1. Charterhouse Distribution Company has all its methods for doing work in the office and warehouse written down; these prescribed methods are ____ .

1. _____

2. Successful planning and operating depend on first establishing clear ____ by deciding what the operating unit should try to accomplish.

2. _____

3. Policies usually are developed and adopted by ____, especially when the policies are to be written down.

3. _____

4. The monthly operating budget of the machine shop is an example of a(n) ____ plan.

4. _____

5. ___ plans are almost always decided on by high-level managers who are trying to shape the overall growth and development of the company.

5. _____

6. ____ is a graphic technique for planning, which shows the relationship between various tasks and critical bottlenecks that may delay a project.

6. _____

7. Joyce has found that the use of a ____ chart is an effective method to assign work equitably to her clerical and office workers.

8. Special rules and orders are examples of ____ set forth by management to restrict the conduct of units within the organization.

9. Gantt is credited with the development of the first ____.

10. ____ brings the planning process right down to the shop floor.

7. _____

8. _____

9. _____

10. _____

Part B: TRUE-FALSE   By writing T or F in the space provided, indicate whether each statement is true or false.

Answers

1. Extending the length of overtime does not affect work output.

1. ____

2. A Gantt chart is used only for production scheduling.

2. ____

3. A work-distribution chart indicates how much work a department can handle with its present staff.

3. ____

4. It is a good idea for a supervisor to set goals that are beyond the ability of the work unit to achieve; this increases workers' determination and motivation.

4. ____

5. The following statement is an example of a quantitative goal: "Decrease the number of service complaints by 6 percent."

5. ____

6. As a general rule, it is a good idea for a supervisor to give employees the reasons and justifications for adopting work unit goals and plans.

6. ____

7. Bobby, who supervises the mixing room, will usually be more concerned with long-range plans than will Grace, who is the corporation's vice president for finance.

7. ____

8. Since the main purpose of controls is to keep operations going according to plans, a supervisor must set control limits when planning.

8. ____

9. In general, policies, especially written ones, apply only at the upper-management levels of a company.

9. ____

10. Joe tells his workers, "If you don't keep a good attendance record, we'll take disciplinary action." This is a good interpretation of company policy.

10. ____

Part C: MULTIPLE CHOICE   Choose the response that best completes each statement. Write the letter of the response in the space provided.

1. Of the following, the best example of a goal is

   Answers

   a. Employees will maintain and sharpen their own hand equipment during regular work hours.
   b. Our company will exercise fair and reasonable controls to regulate the conduct of employees.
   c. The department will produce 15,000 units during the next month.
   d. No equipment or material may be set inside the areas in the plant marked with yellow striping.

   1. ____

2. Of the following, the best example of a rule is
   a. Everyone who enters the construction area must wear protective headgear.
   b. Employees may each decide whether faulty products should be scrapped or reworked.
   c. The waste of materials should be reduced by 5 percent.
   d. All of the above.   2. ____

3. The first step in the planning process should be
   a. Establishing procedures.
   b. Setting goals.
   c. Developing budgets.
   d. Making work assignments.   3. ____

4. The goals of an operating unit within an organization are usually
   a. Long-term, exceeding one year.
   b. Derived only from the specific work tasks of the unit.
   c. Meant to implement the broader and longer-term goals of the entire organization.
   d. Set solely by the supervisor in charge of the unit.   4. ____

5. To be effective, plans should be
   a. Unchanging; otherwise, operations get out of control.
   b. Freely changed whenever even slight obstacles to meeting goals are encountered.
   c. Reviewed regularly to find whether adjustments are needed to respond to changed conditions.
   d. Limited strictly to short terms of less than one month.   5. ____

6. In most companies, general employment practices would follow a
   a. Single-use plan.
   b. Short-term plan.
   c. Long-term plan.
   d. Standing plan.   6. ____

7. An advantage of the PERT chart is that it
   a. Enables planners to identify bottlenecks in complex plans or programs.
   b. Focuses on the deadline.
   c. Focuses on one thing at a time.
   d. Is used mostly in office work.   7. ____

8. The general rule about company policies is that they
   a. Apply mostly to personnel matters and are set and used only by supervisors.
   b. Have little to do with supervisors, since they are set and used mainly by higher management levels.
   c. Are set at higher management levels but are actually turned into action by supervisors.
   d. Should be communicated to workers by supervisors but will have little practical effect on operations.   8. ____

9. In a properly run operating department, who will employees see as the representative of company policy?
   a. The supervisor.
   b. The plant or site manager.
   c. The company's top management.
   d. The shop steward or union representative.   9. ____

10. In nearly any company, what will a supervisor's employees be most interested in knowing about policy?
    a. What is written in the policy manual.
    b. The company's reasons for setting top-level policies.
    c. How policies support department-level operating goals.
    d. The specific and concrete effects on employees of policies.   10. ____

<table>
<tr><td>CHAPTER</td><td>5</td><td>Problem Solving and Managing Information</td></tr>
</table>

LEARNING OBJECTIVES

After studying this chapter, you should be able to

1. Recognize and define a problem or a potential problem.

2. List the eight steps in problem solving and decision making that lead to the removal of a problem's cause.

3. Discuss the rational and intuitive approaches to decision making and explain cost-benefit analysis, decision trees, and ABC analysis.

4. Describe a management information system and differentiate between data and information.

5. Understand how supervisors can create their own departmental information systems.

6. Discuss the impact on employees of computerized information handling systems and suggest ways to alleviate the stress associated with systematization.

CHAPTER STUDY GUIDE OUTLINES

Based on your study of the text chapter and/or your instructor's lesson presentation, complete the following outlines by supplying the correct answers for the numbered spaces. Some answers require more than one word to complete. Write the answers in the numbered answer column. Although you should rely principally on your recollection, you can use the textbook if you need help. Check your answers by referring to the key at the back of this study guide.

1 Problems: Cause and Effect

CONCEPT   Problems in organizations occur because of change, and they are revealed by gaps between expected and actual outcomes.

Answers

1. A __(1)__ has several defining characteristics
   a. Unsettled matter or disturbing condition.
   b. Raises puzzling questions as to its specific nature.
   c. Demands resolution by decisive __(2)__.
   d. Proper settlement is often difficult and uncertain.
   e. May require considerable thought and skill to solve effectively.

1. _____

2. _____

2. A simpler definition is that a problem exists when there is a difference between an expected or hoped for condition and the __(3)__ condition.
   a. Supervisors may solve as many as __(4)__ problems a day.
   b. A great majority of a supervisor's problems are __(5)__.
3. Problems can be classified as
   a. __(6)__ problems, which need immediate solutions to correct what has happened or is happening now.
   b. Potential problems, which are important to identify in __(7)__ to permit preventive problem solving.
4. Problems exist when there is a __(8)__ or variance (a gap) between actual and expected __(9)__. (See Figure 5-1 in the text.)

3. _____
4. _____

5. _____

6. _____

7. _____
8. _____
9. _____

2 ▶ Systematic Problem Solving

CONCEPT   Problems should be approached systematically, with the goal of removing their causes.

1. Problems are solved by __(10)__ whatever it is that has caused, or will cause, a gap between the expected (or desired) condition and the actual condition.
2. Decision making is required whenever there is a __(11)__ to be made when solving a problem.
3. An eight-step approach to systematic problem solving is outlined (see Figure 5-2 in the text).
   a. State the problem clearly and specifically.
   b. Collect all __(12)__ relevant to the problem.
   c. List as many possible __(13)__ for the problem as you can think of.
   d. Select the cause or causes that seem __(14)__.
   e. Suggest as many possible __(15)__ for removing causes or overcoming obstacles.
   f. Evaluate the pros and cons of each proposed solution.
   g. Choose the solution you think is best.
   h. Spell out a __(16)__ to carry out your solution.
4. Table 5–1 in the text is a good guide for determining when to seek help in problem solving.

10. _____

11. _____

12. _____
13. _____

14. _____
15. _____

16. _____

▶3 *Decision Making: Rational and Intuitive*

CONCEPT   Decisions are the logical outcome of problem solving.

1. The systematic (rational) approach to decision making takes place during steps 6 and 7 of problem solving.
   a. Give some weight to your __(17)__ before making a final choice.
   b. Decisions affecting the future contain a degree of __(18)__ that logic cannot fully remove.

2. Mathematical decision making is the use of mathematical, statistical, or quantitative techniques to aid decision making.
   a. Techniques do not make decisions.
   b. Numerical information should be arranged in such a way as to permit decision making based on an interpretation of results.

3. A __(19)__ is a graphic portrait of steps 5 and 6 in the problem-solving process (see Figure 5-3 in the text).
   a. Shows how each __(20)__ leads to various possibilities.
   b. Helps the supervisor visualize various outcomes.
   c. Helps choose the alternative that has the best chance of being effective.

4. __(21)__ adds all the costs of implementation and balances them with the value of the services.
   a. It is often used in the __(22)__ sector.
   b. It is similar to input-output analysis.
   c. In the public sector, excess of benefits is a surplus; in the private sector, it is a __(23)__.

5. Some decisions are based on intuition or hunches.
   a. Many such decisions have paid off.
   b. Such decisions are hard to defend if they go wrong.
   c. Many authorities believe the best decisions come from the dual approach of __(24)__.

6. __(25)__ decisions are spelled out in advance by a standard procedure to react to problems that appear on a recurring basis.
   a. Success of this approach depends on the supervisor correctly identifying the problem.
   b. It can be risky not to consider other solutions.

17. _____

18. _____

19. _____

20. _____

21. _____

22. _____

23. _____

24. _____
25. _____

7. Groups should be involved in decision making when __(26)__ of these factors exist:

   a. Group can provide information, know how, or viewpoints you __(27)__ but don't have.

   b. You respect their opinions and are willing to __(28)__ on their suggestions.

   c. Participation will induce __(29)__ by the group to implement the decision.

   d. You have plenty of __(30)__ .

8. Decisions can be made more effective by

   a. Picking your spots.

     (1) You should try to make decisions only when the potential payoff is great.

     (2) ABC analysis is based on the economic fact that a small number of problems have the potential for the __(31)__ (also known as the 20/80 syndrome), and you should focus your attention on those problems. (See Figure 5-4 in the text.)

   b. Maintaining your __(32)__: you will win some and lose some.

     (1) Don't reach too high.

     (2) Don't overcommit or overextend your resources.

     (3) Always prepare a __(33)__ position.

26. _____

27. _____

28. _____

29. _____

30. _____

31. _____

32. _____

33. _____

4 ▶ Information as a Raw Material

CONCEPT Information is the substance with which problems are solved and decisions are made.

1. Keep looking for information until the cost of __(34)__ it exceeds its __(35)__ .

2. The goal of a __(36)__ (MIS) is to tie a company's past and future data into a library with instant electronic recall.

   a. MIS can be compared to an __(37)__ system that can rapidly accumulate and sort more complex data.

   b. MIS is a network of __(38)__, as well as manual, data processing procedures used by managers to carry out their work.

3. Data are facts and figures that, until processed, bear little relation to decision making.

4. __(39)__ is data processed for specific use by managers in decision making.

34. _____

35. _____

36. _____

37. _____

38. _____

39. _____

5▶ *An MIS of Your Own*

CONCEPT   Supervisors are vital participants in an organization's management information system.

1. They may be __(40)__ who need to understand how to use the information that is generated.

40. _____

2. They may be a prime source of __(41)__ and need to know when and how information is collected and transmitted.

41. _____

3. They can and should design their own MIS.

   a. Figures 5-5(a) and 5-5(b) in the text show how a supervisor would tailor a general system to his or her own department.

   b. __(42)__ is information that is collected and analyzed for the specific purpose of running a particular operation.

42. _____

   c. __(43)__ is any useful information published by an outside source.

43. _____

6▶ *Keeping the System Human*

CONCEPT   Computerized handling of information introduces problems of stress and adjustment to a supervisor's workforce.

1. Systematic (especially computerized) handling of information can have the following positive or negative effects on people at work.

   a. Reduces job tensions and conflicts by making things more orderly.

   b. Creates __(44)__ because it requires individuals to fit their work to a rigid format.

44. _____

   c. Tends to make work __(45)__ because it reduces the opportunity to be creative. People who prefer routine to initiative may like this.

45. _____

   d. Depersonalizes work—people serve machines more than machines serve people; this is especially true at lower levels of the organization.

2. Three ways to make employees more adaptable to the MIS process and computers in general:

   a. Reduce tension by allowing employees to bring their __(46)__ into the open.

46. _____

   b. Acknowledge that it is __(47)__ to be fearful of what the computer may do to jobs and job security.

47. _____

   c. Focus your attention on trying to make sure that people are assigned to the work they do best and like best.

COMMENTARY ON SELF-APPRAISAL FROM THE TEXT

This self-appraisal is aimed at some basic concepts, such as (1) problem recognition, (2 and 3) change as causes, (4) removal of causes to close gaps, (5) finiteness of problem definition, (6) need for considering alternatives, (7) decisions as an essential segment of the problem-solving process, (8) visual function of decision trees, (9) need for intuition as well as logic, (10) value of ABC analysis in identifying the "vital few," (11) contribution of information to problem solving, (12) information as an extension of data—"value-added" data, (13) supervisory role in MIS, (14) distinction between primary and secondary data, and (15) recognition of a genuine need to communicate openly and sympathetically with employees whose jobs are affected by computer systems and MIS.

SELF-CHECK OF YOUR PROGRESS

Part A: COMPLETION An important term or phrase is needed to complete each of the following statements. Write the missing term in the space provided in the answer column.

Answers

1. In any organization, the central cause of problems is ____.

1. _____

2. Because decisions affecting the future contain a degree of uncertainty, give some weight to your ____ before making a final choice.

2. _____

3. A(n) ____ approach nearly always yields the best results in problem solving.

3. _____

4. An effective problem-solving process always ends with ____.

4. _____

5. The ____ is intended to show graphically how alternative decisions interact with possible alternative future conditions.

5. _____

6. An important use of ____ is in deciding the areas of operations in which systematic analysis, problem solving, and decision making will prove most beneficial.

6. _____

7. A(n) ____ decision can be made with less analysis because it applies to situations that have occurred before and for which a solution has already been developed.

7. _____

8. A sales order, an invoice from a vendor, a charge against a credit card account, or a tally of the day's production output is a(n) ____.

8. _____

9. Information collected and analyzed for the specific purpose of running a particular operation or solving a specific problem is ____ data.

9. _____

10. ____ collects and analyzes information about recent developments, production, marketing, and finance for use in decision making.

10. _____

Name _____ Date _____

Part B: TRUE-FALSE By writing T or F in the space provided, indicate whether each statement is true or false.

Answers

1. Any kind of change, whether planned or unplanned, can create problems.

1. ____

2. It is generally a good idea to approach problem solving in a systematic fashion.

2. ____

3. Effective problem solving always requires making at least one and sometimes many decisions.

3. ____

4. Marie considers "Let sleeping dogs lie" to be a good management rule; she never takes action unless a crisis forces her to. Marie's inaction in itself is a decision she has made.

4. ____

5. Since in major decisions so much of the relevant information is unknown, a systematic problem-solving approach has no advantage over an unsystematic approach.

5. ____

6. A search for causes of problems should be made before possible solutions are developed.

6. ____

7. Primary data is any useful information that is published by the government, trade associations, or magazines.

7. ____

8. Michael strictly limits his decision making to situations where there is adequate information for using mathematical methods. Michael's department is probably extremely well managed.

8. ____

9. Supervisors should involve their work groups in decision making when they need to make decisions quickly and they do not have much time to spend on the problem.

9. ____

10. One way to reduce tension about computerization is to allow employees to bring their irritations into the open.

10. ____

Part C: MULTIPLE CHOICE Choose the response that best completes each statement. Write the letter of the response in the space provided.

Answers

1. In which function of the management process does problem solving play an important role?
   a. Planning.
   b. Directing.
   c. Controlling.
   d. All of the above.

1. ____

2. Of the following, the term that is most closely associated with decision making is
   a. Choice.
   b. Causes.
   c. Problems.
   d. Opportunity.

2. ____

3. The final step of the problem-solving process is
   a. Choosing a solution.
   b. Decision making.
   c. Planning and carrying out actions.
   d. Evaluating solutions.

3. ____

4. Decision trees and payoff tables are valuable in that they
   a. Make the decision-making process automatic.
   b. Eliminate the need for making estimates of future outcomes.
   c. Force the decision maker to look realistically at possible outcomes.
   d. All of the above.

4. ____

5. Supervisors are involved in computer operations as
   a. End users.
   b. Prime sources of input.
   c. Principal designers of data systems.
   d. Both a and b above.   5. ____
6. The day's production output for a bicycle factory is
   a. Primary data.
   b. Information.
   c. Secondary data.
   d. MIS.   6. ____
7. The bottom line—the main justification—for the existence of MIS is to
   a. Keep filing systems from becoming too large.
   b. Help managers in decision making.
   c. Centralize the files.
   d. Expedite communications.   7. ____
8. Programmed decisions
   a. Can save the supervisor time and effort.
   b. Can be used only when the present situation has also occurred in the past.
   c. Still require the supervisor to develop a clear understanding of the problem.
   d. All of the above.   8. ____
9. In problem solving and decision making, the supervisor must
   a. Achieve a very high level of successful decisions, at least 90 to 95 percent.
   b. Not be particularly concerned about the outcome of decisions; keeping things
      moving is the key.
   c. Plan to win some and lose some; many solutions will achieve only moderate suc-
      cess.
   d. Be certain not to put a solution into effect unless it is sure to succeed.   9. ____
10. One thing that a supervisor must learn about solving problems is to
    a. Look at the whole picture before deciding whether to seek help or find a solu-
       tion alone.
    b. Always get help before making decisions.
    c. Take full responsibility for making all decisions; no one else is likely to be able
       to contribute.
    d. Pass all decisions of any importance on to the boss.   10. ____

CHAPTER

6 Organizing an Effective Department

LEARNING OBJECTIVES

After studying this chapter, you should be able to

1. Describe the organizing process and its outcome, and differentiate between formal and informal organizations.

2. Identify and differentiate among various organizational structures and formats including functional, line-and-staff, divisional or product, matrix, and centralized and decentralized organizations.

3. Define *authority, responsibility,* and *accountability* and explain their relationships.

4. Understand the benefits to be derived from delegation and explain several effective approaches to it.

5. Discuss the relationship of the organizing process to the chain of command and explain the concept of organizational culture.

CHAPTER STUDY GUIDE OUTLINES

Based on your study of the text chapter and/or your instructor's lesson presentation, complete the following outlines by supplying the correct answers for the numbered spaces. Some answers require more than one word to complete. Write the answers in the numbered answer column. Although you should rely principally on your recollection, you can use the textbook if you need help. Check your answers by referring to the keys at the back of this study guide.

1 ▶ Organizing for Effectiveness

CONCEPT Organizing arranges jobs and groups of jobs in a department so that employees can perform their work in the most effective way.

1. Organizations are groups of people working toward common __(1)__ .

a. Goals may include

   (1) Earning profits for stockholders and wages for employees.

   (2) Supplying goods and services.

   (3) Obtaining personal satisfaction.

Answers

1. _____

b. Organizing is the process of arranging the pattern of __(2)__.
   (1) Lack of organization would create havoc at work.
   (2) An overriding value is the ability to make better use of __(3)__.
   (3) Informal organizations created by employees occur within the formal organizational structure.
c. Planning organizational objectives precedes organizing.
   (1) List all tasks to be done.
   (2) Divide tasks into groups; __(4)__ can accomplish a job.
   (3) Group related jobs together in a logical and efficient manner.
   (4) Establish relationships between jobs and groups of jobs so that all employees have a clear idea of their __(5)__, and of either their dependence on, or control over, people in other jobs or groups of jobs.
2. The best organizations are __(6)__, putting people together so the work gets done better, more quickly, and more cheaply than any other way.

2. _____

3. _____

4. _____

5. _____

6. _____

► *Types of Organizational Structures*

CONCEPT   Organizational structures follow several traditional patterns.

1. Functional, or __(7)__, organizations gather related activities under one functional head (see Figure 6-1 in the text).
2. Line-and-staff organizations add staff groups that provide __(8)__ for the line functions (see Figure 6-2 in the text).
   a. Supervisors in line departments are responsible for getting things __(9)__ (for example, production, sales, deposits, premium collections, fleet operations, nursing).
   b. Supervisors in __(10)__ departments help line departments decide what to do and how to do it. They coordinate and provide service (advisers) to all efforts (for example, accounting, personnel, research, housekeeping, advertising).

7. _____

8. _____

9. _____

10. _____

3. Functional segmentation along with a line-and-staff format.
   a. Divisional or __(11)__: all the functions needed to make a particular product are placed under one highly placed manager (see Figure 6-3 in the text).
   b. __(12)__ regions.
   c. Customer—(for example, farmers, contractors, and homeowners).
   d. Matrix—permits the __(13)__ to use other functional specialists for a short period of time (horizontal authority). Those employees maintain their functional managers as well. This type is best for one-of-a-kind projects (see Figure 6-4 in the text).
4. Centralized versus decentralized organizations.
   a. Centralized organizations have __(14)__ of management, exert tighter controls, and allow employees fewer freedoms to make decisions.
   b. Decentralized organizations have few levels of management, have looser controls, and give employees more freedom of action.
5. __(15)__ .
   a. Supervisors generally should have responsibility for no more than six separate activities.
   b. The actual number should be modified based on the amount of complexity and the level of specialization.
6. Organizational charts explain organizational relationships.
   a. Organizational structures and staffing change __(16)__.
   b. __(17)__ relationships and actual communication patterns are not reflected on organizational charts.

11. _____

12. _____

13. _____

14. _____

15. _____

16. _____
17. _____

▶3 *Authority, Responsibility, and Accountability*

CONCEPT   The organizational structure provides the framework for the formal distribution—or delegation—of authority and responsibility.

1. __(18)__ are those things you are held accountable for.
2. __(19)__ is the power you need to carry out your responsibilities.
   a. Authority is handed down from supervisors—delegation.
   b. Appendix B, "Supervisory Responsibility Survey," in the text provides a checklist to identify a supervisor's responsibility.

18. _____
19. _____

c. In addition to your organizational "right" to act, you also have more personal sources to draw on for getting things done.
   (1) Job knowledge.
   (2) Personal influence.
   (3) __(20)__ .
   (4) Ability to get things done.
   (5) Empathetic and persuasive ability.

20. _____

3. Supervisors can assign responsibility—but they cannot delegate authority.
4. There are three types of authority:
   a. Class 1. Complete authority, taking action without consulting supervisors.
   b. Class 2. __(21)__ , within company policy as long as they notify superiors of the action afterward.
   c. Class 3. No authority, taking no action until they have consulted a superior and received their approval.

21. _____

5. In each of the three types of authority just listed, existing company policy would still prevail.
6. There are special relationships between staff departments and line supervisors.
   a. Line supervisors should make full use of staff department knowledge.
   b. Some departments have __(22)__ , entitling them to specify policy or procedure to be followed in their area of expertise.
   c. Some organizations give supervisors final authority but require prior consultation or agreement with the staff specialist before taking action.

22. _____

▶ Delegation for Leverage

CONCEPT   Delegation of selected tasks by supervisors can greatly add to their personal effectiveness.

1. Delegate when you can't keep up with everything you feel needs to be done.
   a. Start with minor time-consuming tasks.
   b. Delegate routine matters requiring minimal authority (for example, requisitions, reports, calculations, running errands).
2. Effective delegation allows you to concentrate on the __(23)__ yourself.
   a. Be prepared to give up work you enjoy.
   b. Be more concerned with getting the job done right than with who does it.

23. _____

3. There are some things supervisors should not delegate:
   a. Tasks that involve technical knowledge or skills possessed only by the supervisor.
   b. __(24)__ information.

   24. _____

   c. Overloading employees by delegating too much.
   d. The employee __(25)__ process.

   25. _____

4. Take the following steps when delegating:
   a. Give a clear statement concerning responsibilities, authority, and __(26)__ of the task.

   26. _____

   b. Tell the employee why you delegated the job.
   c. Let all employees know that you gave the assignment and that you expect their cooperation.
5. From an employee's perspective, delegation is
   a. A chance to learn a new job.
   b. An opportunity for more job satisfaction.
   c. A reward for other work well done.
6. Potential delegation problems are
   a. Delegating the dirty work.
   b. Overloading a subordinate.
   c. Failing to match responsibility with authority.
   d. __(27)__ or overcontrolling.

   27. _____

5▶ Guidelines for Organizing

> **CONCEPT** Organizing respects the principles of management while providing an important clue to the organization's culture.

1. Delegation should generally follow the __(28)__, or "channels."

   28. _____

   a. Going through channels prevents feeling that you're going over the boss's head.
   b. In emergency or situations of time pressure, you may need to violate the chain of command.
   c. For the purposes of keeping people informed, there is nothing wrong with talking with other departments as long as you don't betray __(29)__.

   29. _____

2. When organizing, don't
   a. Let the chain of command get __(30)__.

   30. _____

   b. Ask one person to report to two bosses.
   c. Make fuzzy job assignments.
   d. Be too rigid.

3. Organizational culture is the underlying set of assumptions, beliefs, attitudes, and expectations shared by members of an organization.
   a. Provides important signals regarding acceptable behavior.
   b. Different cultures can emerge in different divisions or departments.
   c. Clues to an organization's culture can be found in a company's history, its heroines and heroes, its slogans and myths, its common rites and ceremonies.
   d. Most organizational cultures are
      (1) Implicit and fuzzy.
      (2) Relatively stable.
      (3) The product of top management beliefs and visions for the future.
      (4) A powerful factor affecting employee behavior.

COMMENTARY ON SELF-APPRAISAL FROM THE TEXT

This self-appraisal not only provides a straightforward matching exercise in terminology, but also tests your ability to interpret the text material and thus extends your comprehension. It also discourages superficiality by stimulating you to read the text in greater depth. As with all terminology for management and business, it is a good idea to remember that you may encounter difficult terms—or different interpretations of these terms—according to where you work. This text tries to present only generally accepted terminology and definitions.

SELF-CHECK OF YOUR PROGRESS

Part A: COMPLETION   An important term or phrase is needed to complete each of the following statements. Write the missing term in the space provided in the answer column.

Answers

1. The process of dividing the total amount of work to be completed by an organization among its members is called ____ .

1. _____

2. Probably the most important tool for an organization in efficiently reaching its goals is the effective use of ____.

2. _____

3. Staff employees serve as ____ to line employees such as production supervisors.

3. _____

4. The supervisor's act of giving responsibility and authority to a subordinate is ____ .

4. _____

5. An employee is following the ____ when he makes a request to his supervisor for a salary increase rather than going directly to the vice president of human resources.

5. _____

6. The purpose of an organization chart is to help an employee understand the ____ among various departments and different levels within the organization.

6. _____

7. The task force or ____ organization is an organizational structure that might be seen especially in project-oriented work such as that found in a research and development firm.

7. _____

8. The assignment of responsibilities to an employee is useless without the delegation of ____ to carry out those responsibilities.

8. _____

9. The number of activities or people the single manager can supervise is referred to as ____.

9. _____

10. The government sales manager and the agricultural sales manager are responsible to the vice president of sales in a(n) ____ organizational design.

10. _____

Part B: TRUE-FALSE By writing T or F in the space provided, indicate whether each statement is true or false.

Answers

1. The management skill of an assembly-line supervisor in a packaging plant is imperative to that company's success.

1. ____

2. Carl Schmidt is an accountant in a medium-sized corporation. While his supervisor was on vacation, he directly approached the controller about some long-standing management problems in the department. Schmidt was correct in sidestepping the chain of command in this way.

2. ____

3. A company's organization chart should be frequently updated.

3. ____

4. Vivian Jones, the office manager for a large law firm, purposely disregarded the ideas of and the information relationships among the secretaries and law clerks when she revised the firm's internal structure. She was probably correct in doing this.

4. ____

5. In general, any member of management can delegate responsibility and authority.

5. ____

6. Normally, a supervisor should allow one employee to appraise another.

6. ____

7. Decentralized organizations have fewer levels and often can give more individual freedom to their managers and employees.

7. ____

8. The Bauman Company has two divisions: a government purchasers division and a consumer sales division. This is an example of a product organization.

8. ____

9. A company president is not ultimately accountable for lost profits caused by management errors on the part of supervisors down the line.

9. ____

10. It is generally poor management practice to fail to give workers the responsibility that they are capable of and desirous of handling.

10. ____

Part C: MULTIPLE CHOICE Choose the response that best completes each statement. Write the letter of the response in the space provided.

Answers

1. Making a list of all the tasks that must be performed by the organization to accomplish its objectives is the first step in
   a. Organizing.
   b. Organizational culture.
   c. Division of labor.
   d. Planning.

1. ____

2. On an organization chart, boxes that enclose ____ tend to descend from the top of the chart to the bottom in vertical chains.
   a. Production jobs.
   b. Staff departments.
   c. Line departments.
   d. Marketing jobs.

   2. ____

3. A ____ organization is frequently used by research and development or engineering firms for a one-time project or contract.
   a. Matrix.
   b. Centralized.
   c. Divisional.
   d. Decentralized.

   3. ____

4. ____ is defined by the number of activities for which a manager can effectively assume responsibility or by the number of employees he or she can effectively supervise.
   a. Span of control.
   b. Delegation.
   c. Organizational culture.
   d. Accountability.

   4. ____

5. Although it doesn't take direct action itself, which department can exert influence by advising and guiding?
   a. Production.
   b. Marketing.
   c. Line.
   d. Staff.

   5. ____

6. The underlying set of assumptions, beliefs, attitudes, and expectations shared by members of an organization describe
   a. Organizational culture.
   b. Staff departments.
   c. Span of control.
   d. Delegation.

   6. ____

7. An organization's overriding value lies in its ability to make more effective use of
   a. Span of control.
   b. Human resources.
   c. Authority.
   d. Responsibility.

   7. ____

8. Which is the path that information, directives, or instructions follow through the chain of command?
   a. A line.
   b. A channel.
   c. Delegation.
   d. Staff.

   8. ____

9. Responsibility without ____ in effect makes the supervisor powerless.
   a. Delegation.
   b. A job description.
   c. Authority.
   d. Accountability.

   9. ____

10. To be successful, the supervisor must be good at
    a. Staffing.
    b. Delegation.
    c. Planning.
    d. All of the above.

    10. ____

CHAPTER 7 Staffing With Human Resources

LEARNING OBJECTIVES

After studying this chapter, you should be able to

1. Know the factors that affect workforce requirements, and understand the implications of overstaffing and understaffing.

2. Identify the five steps of the staffing process and explain the extent of a supervisor's participation in each.

3. Discuss the critical aspects of the selection process and the role of application blanks, tests, and reference checks.

4. Explain the main features of an employment interview and identify the types of questions that are most suitable and those areas that are restricted by equal employment opportunity legislation.

5. Explain how careful selection can reduce employee turnover and absences, and show how to calculate specified turnover and absenteeism measures.

CHAPTER STUDY GUIDE OUTLINES

Based on your study of the text chapter and/or your instructor's lesson presentation, complete the following outlines by supplying the correct answers for the numbered spaces. Some answers require more than one word to complete. Write the answers in the numbered answer column. Although you should rely principally on your recollection, you can use the textbook if you need help. Check your answers by referring to the keys at the back of this study guide.

1 ▶ Forecasting Workforce Requirements

CONCEPT   Effective staffing helps meet performance goals, but it depends on careful analysis of work requirements and needs for employees.

Answers

1. Supervisors should be concerned about the __(1)__ process.
   a. People are an organization's most vital __(2)__. They
      (1) Make or break departmental __(3)__.
      (2) Are very __(4)__ resources.
      (3) Should be selected very carefully.
      (4) Should receive __(5)__ by their supervisor after their hiring.

1. _____

2. _____

3. _____

4. _____

5. _____

b. Effective staffing can __(6)__ departmental performance. It includes

    (1) Estimating the number of workers needed to staff the department.

    (2) Playing an active and educated role in selecting the employees hired by the organization.

    (3) Maintaining the __(7)__ that attract and hold the best employees.

2. Workforce forecasting includes six major steps:

  a. Find out what your department is expected to __(8)__ within a specific time period.

  b. __(9)__ how much the work schedule means in terms of total worker-hours.

  c. Convert total hours to worker-days by dividing the number of hours in the standard workday. Then, divide the total by the number of working days during the period to find the number of employees needed.

  d. Determine the number of __(10)__ (maintenance, setup persons, etc.) and add the number of direct employees needed to get the total needed.

  e. Make allowances for absences, training, and leaves.

  f. Search for other ways to meet your schedule including overtime, transfers or borrowed employees, stretching initial timeliness for job completion, and using __(11)__ employees during peak demand periods.

3. Your goal is to make sure the number of employees on hand matches the __(12)__ .

  a. __(13)__ results in departmental costs going up and efficiency suffering.

    (1) Slight overstaffing offers flexibility during production emergencies and greater opportunities for coaching, training, and team building.

  b. __(14)__ can get you behind in the schedule and undermine the effort to engage in time-based competition.

    (1) Short-term understaffing can stimulate creativity.

6. _____

7. _____

8. _____
9. _____

10. _____

11. _____

12. _____
13. _____

14. _____

▶ The Staffing Process

CONCEPT   Effective staffing places the right numbers—and kinds—of workers on the right jobs at the right times through a systematic process.

1. Organizational staffing is accomplished through a five-step procedure:

  a. Specifying the kinds of __(15)__ and workers needed.

15. _____

b. __(16)__ the number of employees needed to complete a work schedule.

c. __(17)__ job candidates.

d. Preliminary __(18)__ of job candidates.

e. Selecting the most appropriate job __(19)__.

2. __(20)__ decisions can be improved by

   a. Careful job analysis.

   b. __(21)__ seeking relevant information about work experience and education.

   c. Preliminary screening __(22)__.

   d. Employment __(23)__.

   e. Wide variety of psychological, knowledge, honesty, performance, and medical __(24)__.

3. Application blanks can solicit relevant information about experience, specific skills, speed and accuracy, and __(25)__.

4. Properly chosen, administered, and interpreted employment tests can help pick employees. Performance tests measure the ability of applicants to do the major parts of the job.

   a. All tests used should be fully __(26)__ and their reliability established before they are used.

      (1) This is necessary to meet __(27)__ and increase the likelihood of desirable selection decisions.

   b. Validity means the test measures what it is supposed to measure.

   c. __(28)__ means it can do that measurement consistently.

   d. Tests should also be relevant to the job's content, not discriminate unfairly, and not unduly invade applicant's privacy.

5. Medical evaluations should occur __(29)__ employment decisions have been made.

   a. Supervisors may ask if there is a physical or mental impairment that makes it impossible to __(30)__ the work.

6. Supervisors should look for ways to provide __(31)__ that would allow differently abled persons to succeed on the job.

7. Supervisors should check employee references.

   a. Verify the actual job the applicant held and the dates of employment.

      (1) Many former employers will __(32)__ tell much for fear of illegally prejudicing the applicant's chances.

16. _____

17. _____

18. _____

19. _____

20. _____

21. _____

22. _____

23. _____

24. _____

25. _____

26. _____

27. _____

28. _____

29. _____

30. _____

31. _____

32. _____

(2) Ask the job candidate to sign a __(33)__, which authorizes you to contact personal and employment references, and verify education and employment background.

33. _____

b. __(34)__ references are usually not of much value.

34. _____

3 ▶ Interviewing Job Candidates

CONCEPT   Interview questions should be strictly job related and must be free from any implication of bias.

1. Three purposes of a job interview are to
   a. Provide an __(35)__ of the job and work environment.

35. _____

   (1) Provide information about both favorable and __(36)__ job tasks.

36. _____

   (2) Mention job title, major tasks, relationships to other jobs, and degree of discretion allowed.
   (3) Describe the job environment, equipment, safety, __(37)__, and working conditions.

37. _____

   (4) If possible, show the __(38)__.

38. _____

   (5) Describe opportunities for __(39)__, the organization's benefit programs, etc.

39. _____

   b. Obtain key data that allows you to decide which candidate is the best.
   c. Build a positive relationship with the applicants.
   (1) Build __(40)__, by welcoming and putting the candidate at ease.

40. _____

   (2) Explain your purpose, which is to get information to make a judgment about their prospects for job success.
   (3) Avoid asking __(41)__ or challenging their answers.

41. _____

   (4) Thank them for their time and indicate __(42)__ they will hear about your decision.

42. _____

2. __(43)__ beginning with what, where, why, when, or who make good interview questions.

43. _____

3. Avoid asking questions about race, religion, national origin, __(44)__, age (unless you need to know if the applicant is legally old enough to work for you), marital status, disability or past illnesses (though you may determine if the applicant can perform the primary tasks of the job), __(45)__, and arrests (you may ask about convictions from major crimes).

44. _____

45. _____

◢ 4 ▶ *Making the Selection Decision*

CONCEPT   Use the available information carefully to screen out the less qualified candidates and find the ones with greatest chance of success.

1. Remember, there are __(46)__ you will hire a successful employee.

2. Selection is more like screening "out" the poorer candidates than identifying the best one.

3. You are seeking evidence from __(47)__ that confirms a tentative conclusion.

4. Don't rely on a single selection tool but use multiple items, identified earlier in this chapter.

5. Review the information collected, paying attention to
   a. __(48)__ characteristics.
   b. Problematic attitudes.
   c. __(49)__.

6. When an employee is chosen, consider using the __(50)__ to increase the likelihood that he or she will succeed.
   a. The process of believing something to be true and then acting so as to make it more likely to happen.
   b. It can be used in three ways:
      (1) Tell the chosen candidate that he or she was your first choice.
      (2) Tell your __(51)__ you have selected a new worker with a strong track record and high likelihood of success.
      (3) Remind yourself that your __(52)__ is on the line with every new hire.

46. _____

47. _____

48. _____

49. _____

50. _____

51. _____

52. _____

◢ 5 ▶ *Minimizing the Potential for Absences and Turnover*

CONCEPT   The selection process should seek to minimize the employment of people whose unsuitability will result in excessive absences and/or turnover.

1. High turnover and absenteeism are major indicators of __(53)__ staffing and selection.

2. The high cost of hiring, training, and paying employees makes it important that staffing decisions are done correctly.

3. The __(54)__ compares the total number of separations with the average number of employees on your payroll during a particular period.

53. _____

54. _____

a. The turnover rate is calculated as follows:

(1) $\dfrac{\text{Number of separations} \times 100}{\text{Average size of workforce}} = $ turnover percentage.

b. Turnover rates vary widely. It is important to find out what your employer's past experience is and what is considered acceptable in your situation.

c. Excluding certain types of separations or hires will __(55)__ turnover rates.

d. Know what the specifications are when comparing turnover rates.

4. Turnover is related to employee __(56)__.

a. Poor morale can be a result of having poor supervision and/or having the wrong person in the wrong job.

b. Careful __(57)__ can reduce turnover and result in more effective supervision.

5. __(58)__ is costly to the organization, frequently resulting in the need to hire temporary employees, pay overtime, and delay operations.

a. It is computed as either the average days absent per year or the percentage of scheduled worker-days lost.

b. Good __(59)__ can reduce absenteeism.

c. Careful screening can eliminate applicants who may be absentee problems at your company.

(1) Look for a person who fits the company.

(2) Look for a person who fits the available opening.

55. _____

56. _____

57. _____

58. _____

59. _____

COMMENTARY ON SELF-APPRAISAL FROM THE TEXT

The intention here is to enable you to judge the staffing performance of a supervisor who understands the technical fundamentals pretty well, but who is off base when it comes to understanding some of the human relations and legal aspects of employment interviewing. The items in this exercise are fairly clear cut as to whether they represent good practice. On the basis of the information provided in the text, you should be able to agree with the ratings provided by the experts.

1. Good practice. Tricia should participate actively in step 1 of the staffing process.
2. Good practice. Recruiting is better left to the human resources professionals.
3. Doubtful practice. Interviewing is a prime responsibility of supervisors, and few excuses justify avoiding it.
4. Good practice. See step 5 of the procedure for forecasting workforce size.
5. Good practice. Even a few absences among 20 employees can add up to a significant figure over a year. If each employee lost 5 days, that would be 100 worker-days to be accounted for.
6. Good practice. Overstaffing can be justified to assure completion of critical operations, as dispatching is said to be.

7. Bad practice. Applicants should be told of the unattractive, as well as the desirable, aspects of the work.
8. Bad or doubtful practice. "Yes" or "no" questions close off discussion and the opportunity for the applicant to volunteer information. Open-ended questions are far more desirable.
9. Bad practice. This is discriminatory. Equal opportunity legislation implies that no prejudgments should be made on the basis of sex.
10. Good practice. Apparently, arithmetic skills represent a bona fide occupational qualification, and the use of a reliable, validated test is warranted.

SELF-CHECK OF YOUR PROGRESS

Part A: COMPLETION   An important term is needed to complete each of the following statements. Write the missing term in the space provided in the answer column.

Answers

1. The average number of days an employee is not at work or the percentage of scheduled worker-days lost is your ____ .

1. _____

2. Effective workforce ____ minimizes both layoffs and rehiring.

2. _____

3. ____ tests attempt to find out whether a person has the ability to learn a particular kind of job.

3. _____

4. The number of persons who come to a work for a supervisor and then leave for any reason is referred to as ____ .

4. _____

5. ____ refers to the accuracy with which a test measures what it is supposed to measure.

5. _____

6. Asking about or commenting on a prospective employee's race or national origin is ____ .

6. _____

7. ____ refers to the consistency of the outcome of a test if a job applicant takes it several times.

7. _____

8. Most businesses use a(n) ____ to legally and systematically gather and record information from a job applicant about his or her qualifications, education, and work experience.

8. _____

9. A balanced presentation of positive and negative features about a job is referred to in the text as a ____ .

9. _____

10. A face-to-face exchange of information between a job applicant and an employer's representative is referred to as an employment ____ .

10. _____

Part B: TRUE-FALSE   By writing T or F in the space provided, indicate whether each statement is true or false.

Answers

1. A supervisor's placing the right workers on a job at the right time is indicative of accurately balancing the workforce.

1. ____

2. Attrition is the gradual reduction of the workforce because of natural events and causes such as retirements.

2. ____

3. A typing test for a secretarial candidate is an example of a performance test.

3. ____

4. Personality tests are widely used for applicants seeking higher-level management positions.

4. ____

5. Most former employers will be open and forthright in discussing a past employee's job performance.   5. ___

6. It is illegal to ask a candidate about convictions for major crimes.   6. ___

7. It is usually a waste of time for a supervisor to forecast workforce requirements for the department more than one month ahead.   7. ___

8. The formula used to calculate the absenteeism rate, which is also called the percentage of scheduled days lost, is

$$\frac{\text{total days absent} \times 0.10}{\text{worker-days worked plus worker-days lost}}$$

    8. ___

9. Personal references are usually not of much value.   9. ___

10. An interviewer is legally permitted to ask applicants why they left the last job.   10. ___

Part C: MULTIPLE CHOICE   Choose the response that best completes each statement. Write the letter of the response in the space provided.

Answers

1. In forecasting workforce requirements, the first thing a supervisor must do is to
   a. Determine what the workforce schedule is in terms of total worker-hours.
   b. Determine the average number of days a month workers in the department are absent.
   c. Determine what the production expectations are for the next week, month, or quarter.
   d. Determine the number of workers in the department at a given time.   1. ___

2. If Gary wanted to increase the chances that his new employee will succeed, he should consider doing each of the following things except
   a. Tell the employee he or she was Gary's first choice for the job.
   b. Let the employee know what will happen if he or she doesn't meet his performance standards.
   c. Tell existing employees he selected a new worker with a strong track record.
   d. Ask himself what he can do to help the new employee become productive.   2. ___

3. Which tests are usually dependable in determining a candidate's aptitude for a certain job?
   a. Performance.
   b. Personality.
   c. Aptitude.
   d. Social intelligence.   3. ___

4. The best questions that an interviewer can ask a job candidate are ones that
   a. Require only "yes" or "no" answers.
   b. Are very direct and to the point.
   c. Ask what, where, why, when, and who.
   d. Discourage the candidate from talking too much about himself or herself.   4. ___

5. Felix may require an applicant to take a medical evaluation legally
   a. If it appears the applicant is physically disabled in some way.
   b. If the applicant appears mentally unstable during the interview.
   c. After an employment decision has been made to be sure the applicant can perform the job.
   d. All of the above.   5. ___

6. If you had an average of 50 employees during a month, but laid off 3, what would the turnover rate for that month be?
   a. 3 percent.
   b. 5 percent.
   c. 6 percent.
   d. 9 percent.   6. ____

7. The cost of keeping a semiskilled worker on the payroll for a year is currently estimated to be about
   a. $2,000.
   b. $50,000.
   c. $20,000.
   d. $30,000.   7. ____

8. A supervisor accomplishes her or his goal of achieving departmental performance results by
   a. Estimating the number of workers needed to staff the department.
   b. Playing an active role in selecting employees.
   c. Maintaining working conditions that hold the best employees.
   d. All of the above.   8. ____

9. Which of the following is not a characteristic of understaffing?
   a. Failure to meet schedules.
   b. Employees feeling overworked.
   c. Lack of flexibility for the supervisor.
   d. Ability to step up production in emergencies.   9. ____

10. Each of the following is a step in the staffing process except
    a. Forecasting the number of employees needed to complete a work schedule.
    b. Recruiting candidates for job openings.
    c. Selecting employees from among the candidates.
    d. Calculating absentee rates.   10. ____

CHAPTER

8 Training and Developing Employees

LEARNING OBJECTIVES

After studying this chapter, you should be able to

1. Explain why employees need to be trained and how to identify their needs.

2. Discuss the training roles of supervisors and their relationships with the training department.

3. Identify when employees should be trained, beginning with orientation programs.

4. Understand how employees learn best and how these learning principles can be used in the four-step method of training.

5. Choose appropriate training methods and aids to assist the learning process.

6. Define transfer of training and explain the actions a supervisor can take to ensure that a payoff is received from training.

CHAPTER STUDY GUIDE OUTLINES

Based on your study of the text chapter and/or your instructor's lesson presentation, complete the following outlines by supplying the correct answers for the numbered spaces. Some answers require more than one word to complete. Write the answers in the numbered answer column. Although you should rely principally on your recollection, you can use the textbook if you need help. Check your answers by referring to the keys at the back of this study guide.

1 ▶ Training Needs

CONCEPT   Employees need systematic, guided training that begins with identification of job-related needs.

Answers

1. Formal education and __(1)__ are extremely important today.

    a. An extra year of __(2)__ adds $100,000 to a typical worker's lifetime earnings.

    b. A college education provides a __(3)__ rate of return to the individual.

    c. Training within an organization holds the key to __(4)__ gains and __(5)__ customer service.

2. Structured and systematic training is based on careful study of what a job __(6)__ in terms of knowledge and __(7)__. It involves an orderly period of __(8)__ by a person

1. _____

2. _____

3. _____

4. _____

5. _____

6. _____

7. _____

8. _____

a. Familiar with the job.

b. Well-versed in training techniques.

c. Aware of the __(9)__ process.

9. _____

3. Equipment manufacturer's instruction manuals, outside reading, and __(10)__ instruction can't be relied on to give employees __(11)__ job training.

10. _____

11. _____

a. The percentage of workers who can learn their jobs this way is very small.

b. When combined with personalized instructions by the __(12)__, these methods can be more effective.

12. _____

4. Training needs can be assessed both __(13)__ and informally.

13. _____

a. Informal assessment includes being alert for subpar production rates, too much __(14)__, out-of-line operating costs, accident rates, excessive __(15)__, etc.

14. _____

15. _____

(1) There could also be signs of poor __(16)__, motivation problems, or __(17)__ conditions.

16. _____

17. _____

(2) Interpretation of these symptoms should be supplemented by a formal analysis of __(18)__.

18. _____

b. Formal assessment is more structured and attempts to answer the questions of __(19)__ needs training, __(20)__ do they need, and whether training is a good __(21)__ to performance problems.

19. _____

20. _____

21. _____

(1) Includes surveys, interviews, __(22)__, and observation.

22. _____

(2) If used regularly, can identify trends and make comparisons with other employees or departments.

5. It is important to keep a record of worker training, sometimes called a __(23)__. (See text Figure 8-1.) These inventories

23. _____

a. Record what workers can already __(24)__.

24. _____

b. Indicate what each worker doesn't need to be able to do.

c. __(25)__ for what each worker has to learn.

25. _____

d. Set definite plans for completing training in each part of the job.

▶2 A Training Partnership

CONCEPT   Supervisors are the primary source of employee training, but the training department, skilled coworkers, and the employee are also key partners.

1. Today's supervisor must be a __(26)__, in addition to his or her traditional duties of planning, organizing, motivating, and controlling.

26. _____

a. Employees want to grow and take on new __(27)__ and supervisors must show them how.

27. _____

2. Training by the supervisor goes beyond teaching basic skills to include assisting employees to learn to analyze situations, __(28)__, and integrate new ideas.

28. _____

3. Coaching is an effective way to help employees learn. A supervisor acting as coach
   a. Watches for __(29)__ opportunities.

   29. _____

   b. Demonstrates __(30)__ behaviors.

   30. _____

   c. Asks __(31)__ questions to stimulate thought.

   31. _____

   d. Gives timely feedback in a __(32)__ manner.

   32. _____

4. It is important to remember that training
   a. Needs to be done every __(33)__.

   33. _____

   b. Builds a workforce that returns full value for every dollar __(34)__.

   34. _____

5. Supervisors can share the training responsibility with
   a. A knowledgeable, skilled __(35)__ who has been trained to communicate key points to trainees without overwhelming them.

   35. _____

   b. The trainee can take some responsibility for __(36)__ learning, asking for assistance only when needed.

   36. _____

   c. Even after delegating training responsibilities, the supervisor must continue to oversee training and the trainees to be sure they are meeting expectations.

6. Company training departments can
   a. Identify training needs and specify training programs and methods.
   b. Conduct __(37)__ of training.

   37. _____

   c. Assist supervisors in meeting their training needs.
   d. Conduct training that needs to be __(38)__ across departments (i.e., orientation on company history, new products, literacy training).

   38. _____

   e. Be invaluable with job breakdowns, lesson plans, and training timetables.

3▶ Orientation Training

CONCEPT   New employees need an orientation to their jobs, coworkers, and work environment.

1. Training should begin whenever a new employee is __(39)__.

   39. _____

   a. This gets new workers started on the right foot.
   b. New employees are most receptive to instruction because they want to learn and succeed (teachable moment).

2. __(40)__ sessions should include topics of probable interest as well as items you feel are important to their success.
   a. Pay-related issues.
   b. Hours of work.
   c. Availability of overtime and premium pay.
   d. Time reporting systems.
   e. Fringe-benefit plan and employee options.
   f. Procedure to follow when sick or late.
   g. Basic __(41)__ and reporting procedures.
3. Induction activities should include
   a. Tour of __(42)__ and company.
   b. Introduction to __(43)__.
   c. Assignment to a work area and identification of resources.
   d. Location of cafeteria, lockers, and rest rooms.
   e. Location of first-aid facilities.
4. Ask questions to be sure the employees understand this material; consider giving information out in __(44)__.

40. _____

41. _____

42. _____
43. _____

44. _____

◢4▶ *Factors in Learning*

      CONCEPT   Much is known about how employees learn best, and these ideas should be built into any training program.

1. Knowledge is information that can be learned.
2. __(45)__ is the ability to perform a job-related action using a combination of relevant knowledge and physical and perceptual abilities. It is acquired through guided practice.
3. Breaking a job down for training purposes involves
   a. Observing the job as it is done and __(46)__ it into logical steps.
   b. Identifying the __(47)__ in each step of the job breakdown.
     (1) The key point is the point that might make or break a job or injure the worker. (See text Figure 8-2 and text Table 8-1.)
     (2) Key points can be obtained from manuals, records, and current employees.
4. The best way to teach a job is in a logical order, or start with the __(48)__ part and proceed to the most difficult (see text Figure 8-3).

45. _____

46. _____

47. _____

48. _____

5. The foundation of systematic, structured job training (or job instruction training, JIT) has four cornerstones. In the past, employee specialization was popular, and they were expected to perform a __(49)__ tasks skillfully for a particular job. This approach often led to

    a. Worker boredom.

    b. Inflexibility across employees.

    c. Limited opportunities for __(50)__ and wage increases.

6. A new trend has emerged: __(51)__ pay—has employees acquire skills and demonstrate compctency. They are certified as capable in that job and qualify for a higher rate of pay.

    a. They are more valuable because they can __(52)__ back and forth across multiple jobs.

    b. The variety and challenge keep them __(53)__.

    c. They are always learning something new so the need for __(54)__ never ends.

7. Supervisors get employees to learn

    a. By showing how training can get them ahead, build job security, and increase their incomes.

    b. Showing employees how new jobs and better methods make work more interesting.

    c. Engaging employees' __(55)__ in the training process by showing not only what to do and how to do it, but __(56)__ it needs to be done.

8. When involved in training, remember

    a. People learn at __(57)__ speeds.

    b. Some jobs are more difficult (and more difficult to teach and learn).

    c. Training does not occur at the same __(58)__ for all jobs.

    d. Research indicates that learning disappears __(59)__ unless we keep working at it.

    e. __(60)__ workers can and do learn new methods and new jobs.

        (1) Learning may occur more slowly than with younger workers because of the need to unlearn what they have been taught earlier.

        (2) They may have less incentive to learn new procedures than younger workers.

49. _____

50. _____

51. _____

52. _____

53. _____

54. _____

55. _____

56. _____

57. _____

58. _____

59. _____

60. _____

5 ▶ *Training Methods and Aids*

CONCEPT   Effective training uses a variety of training methods and aids to facilitate employee learning.

1. __(61)__ of a training method depends on
   a. What your objective is—knowledge acquisition or __(62)__.
   b. How much time, space, materials, or special preparation is required.
   c. Whether the training method will make the trainee active or passive.
   d. How many employees must be trained at __(63)__.
2. Training methods include
   a. On-the-job—coaching or job rotation.
   b. Off-the-job—classroom lectures.
   c. __(64)__ blends classroom training with hands-on skill practice under the guidance of experienced coaches.
      (1) May last from one to four __(65)__.
      (2) Trainees are prepared for a variety of job skills even though they may only use a small number of them.
      (3) Programs are not tailored to the __(66)__.
3. __(67)__ help trainees visualize what you are telling them. This __(68)__ up the learning process.
   a. May include transparencies, slides, films, posters, flip charts, and chalkboards.
   b. The best visual aid is actual demonstration on the equipment a worker will use.
   c. Audio cassettes present information to workers during their free time.
   d. Videos can provide both information and realistic demonstrations at the job site.
   e. Computer-assisted instruction is very appealing to trainees but is quite expensive and should be used selectively when its cost can be justified.
   f. A special form of visual aid that is inexpensive and useful is the __(69)__.
      (1) Examples are checklists, flowcharts, worksheets, or listings of step-by-step instructions.
      (2) They minimize the fear of __(70)__ something.
      (3) They are especially useful when a procedure is performed __(71)__, a mistake would be costly, or a supervisor is not close by.
4. Some training can be conducted in small groups, off the job, inexpensively with good success.

61. _____

62. _____

63. _____

64. _____

65. _____

66. _____
67. _____
68. _____

69. _____

70. _____

71. _____

a. This is true when new policies or procedures need to be explained to __(72)__ workers.

72. _____

b. When employees need to know the theory and background behind an operation.

c. The best training methods involve the participants __(73)__ in their learning.

73. _____

5. Programmed learning is another example of off-the-job training.

a. __(74)__, which tests the trainees immediately after they're exposed to a small block of information.

74. _____

b. Trainees move on only after being able to demonstrate mastery of the material.

c. It uses regular feedback to reinforce learning.

6 ▶ Obtaining Results From Training

CONCEPT   Training is useful only if it is transferred to the job and has a demonstrable payoff.

1. Training is expensive, but the alternative is more expensive.

a. __(75)__ costs include training materials, visual aids, and outside instructors.

75. _____

b. __(76)__ costs include the supervisors' and trainees' time, the effect of errors made, and the lost productivity during training.

76. _____

c. The goal of systematic training is to avoid the need to repeat it later.

2. Benefits from training include

a. Improved quality and quantity of output or service.

b. Smooth interdepartmental transfers.

c. More time for other supervisory tasks.

d. A reserve of trained personnel in your department.

e. Increased confidence and cooperation of your workers.

f. A supervisor who is a prime candidate for __(77)__.

77. _____

3. The probability that training will transfer to the job is increased by

a. Discussing the __(78)__ in advance with employees.

78. _____

b. Pointing out effective employees as potential role models.

c. Visibly monitoring trainee __(79)__.

79. _____

d. __(80)__ successful behaviors regularly.

80. _____

e. Giving training the attention it deserves.

4. Major United States companies, recognizing that the workforce of the future will draw more heavily from minority, immigrant, or other disadvantaged groups, urge these guidelines for training of that workforce:

a. Make the training __(81)__.

81. _____

b. Rely on __(82)__.

82. _____

c. Overtrain rather than undertrain.

d. Offer personal aid.

e. Provide lots of followup.

f. Reassure and recognize frequently.

g. Use the __(83)__ system.

83. _____

COMMENTARY ON SELF-APPRAISAL FROM THE TEXT

This exercise encourages you to convert theoretical material about employee learning into applied material, or action principles. Much is known about how people learn but it is not always presented in usable fashion for supervisors. The principles generated here are useful and are related to conceptual material that provide initial skill practice to help you when you confront future concepts. The correct relationship of the eight statements with the action principles for Roxanna is this:

1. Put Greg at ease. This takes off the pressure to perform (immediately). Say that you expect some initial mistakes, which are acceptable as long as he learns from them.

2. Many adult workers are not used to sitting for long hours in classroom-style environments, nor are they capable of absorbing large amounts of new information. Provide Greg with new knowledge in small bits and wait for him to absorb it first.

3. Employees like to see the larger picture and where they fit into it. Give Greg a physical and intellectual "tour" of the total food service operation. Use diagrams and flowcharts to show how it all comes together and where he fits in.

4. In general, train employees how to do it right at first (creating a quality product or service) and then encourage them to develop speed later on.

5. Provide extensive, and regular, feedback to Greg to satisfy his need to know how he is doing. Couple this with positive reinforcement.

6. Even though Greg is inexperienced, chances are he has eaten in several fast-food restaurants and had some reactions to the food and service. Ask him questions and draw on relevant examples to make the training realistic for him.

7. Accept the fact that trainees will learn at different speeds and retain different amounts of what has been taught to them. Similarly, some people learn best through words and concepts, while others learn best through visual diagrams and pictures.

8. Prepare, and share with trainees, a set of objectives specifying what knowledge they must acquire and the skills they will be able to perform after their training.

SELF-CHECK OF YOUR PROGRESS

Part A: COMPLETION   An important term or phrase is needed to complete each of the following statements. Write the missing term in the space provided in the answer column.

Answers

1. Helping new employees to feel comfortable in the new physical environment and explaining company policies and procedures to them is ____.

1. _____

2. Sometimes employees learn through supervisory observation, demonstration, questioning, and feedback. This is an example of ____ .

3. An employee acquires ____ by reading, listening, or observing.

4. A(n) ____ is that knowledge that provides a breakthrough for the worker in successfully completing a task.

5. If employees obtain information at their own pace by consulting resources and asking for guidance when they feel they need it, they are involved in ____ .

6. ____ is the capability to perform a job-related action.

7. ____ are the specific occasions when employees are most receptive to receiving feedback and instructions from their supervisors.

8. A self-administered teaching technique that presents information in readily absorbed bits is called ____ .

9. If you segment a particular job into important steps that the employee must perform to advance or complete work, you have completed ____ analysis.

10. ____ are materials placed on or near the work area that help employees remember key points and perform effectively.

2. _____

3. _____

4. _____

5. _____

6. _____

7. _____

8. _____

9. _____

10. _____

Part B: TRUE-FALSE By writing T or F in the space provided, indicate whether each statement is true or false.

Answers

1. Employees learn effectively whether they are trained systematically or by trial and error.

2. Job training is one of a supervisor's chief responsibilities.

3. A high accident rate and excessive overtime can both be indications that a better or more effective training program is needed.

4. When training workers for a new job, it is better to give them small doses of information.

5. A supervisor has no responsibility in induction training if human resources is involved.

6. The percentage of employees who can learn their jobs by taking only correspondence courses is very small.

7. Training is the only certain way to build a cost-effective workforce.

8. Many companies have found relying on demonstrations will communicate more effectively than words alone with an audience whose verbal skills are underdeveloped.

9. Experienced employees often forget or are unaware of the key points of their job.

10. Older workers have the ability to learn new methods and new jobs.

1. ____

2. ____

3. ____

4. ____

5. ____

6. ____

7. ____

8. ____

9. ____

10. ____

Part C: MULTIPLE CHOICE Choose the response that best completes each statement. Write the letter of the response in the space provided.

Answers

1. Of the four ways available to provide training, the only dependable one is
   a. Trial and error.
   b. Structured and systematic.
   c. Sink or swim.
   d. Hit or miss.

1. ____

2. An example of the informal approach to assessing training needs is
   a. High accident rate.
   b. Skills tests.
   c. Observations of employees at work.
   d. Surveys.   2. ___

3. Nassif wants to maintain a record of each worker's training needs. Which of the following would be an important part of that record?
   a. Indicate what each worker can already do.
   b. Indicate what each worker doesn't need to be able to do.
   c. Plan ahead for what each worker has to learn.
   d. All of the above.   3. ___

4. Jane demonstrated that she had the necessary skill to operate a forklift when she
   a. Said she could operate a manual transmission.
   b. Passed a forklift operator's driving test.
   c. Passed a written safety test.
   d. Passed a written test on the forklift manufacturer's operating instructions.   4. ___

5. When breaking a job down for training purposes, you should
   a. Have several teachable moments to reinforce training.
   b. Divide the job into logical steps.
   c. Involve the manufacturer's sales representative.
   d. All of the above.   5. ___

6. It has been estimated that an extra year of high school adds about this much to a typical worker's lifetime earnings.
   a. Nothing.
   b. $100,000.
   c. $10,000.
   d. $50,000.   6. ___

7. Nancy telling Tom about the hours of work is an example of
   a. A teachable moment.
   b. Apprenticeship training.
   c. Key point training.
   d. Orientation training.   7. ___

8. To be fair to all employees, training should
   a. Occur at the same specd for all employees.
   b. Take place off the job.
   c. Never involve a coworker as a trainer.
   d. Take place at different speeds depending on the situation.   8. ___

9. An inexpensive and useful visual aid is
   a. Computer-assisted instruction.
   b. Interactive videodiscs.
   c. The job aid.
   d. Induction training.   9. ___

10. Butch is a supervisor who wants to move up the managerial ladder. Which of the following things will help him increase his potential for promotion most?
    a. Hire employees that have been through apprenticeship programs.
    b. Give the training department the responsibility for on-the-job training.
    c. Measure employee productivity before and after training.
    d. Use visual aids in training.   10. ___

CHAPTER 9 Motivating People at Work

LEARNING OBJECTIVES

After studying this chapter, you should be able to

1. Recognize some of the factors that influence the development of each person's unique personality.

2. Describe the major needs that employees typically have, and explain how they influence motivation and behavior.

3. Explain the differences between satisfaction and dissatisfaction, and discuss how a supervisor can affect the contributing factors.

4. Understand the concepts of expectancy theory, drives for achievement, power, and affiliation, and the impact of equity and inequity as they affect employee motivation and morale.

5. Identify the elements found in a people-centered approach to job design and explain how, when they are used to empower employees, they provide motivation and improve the quality of work life.

CHAPTER STUDY GUIDE OUTLINES

Based on your study of the text chapter and/or your instructor's lesson presentation, complete the following outlines by supplying the correct answers for the numbered spaces. Some answers require more than one word to complete. Write the answers in the numbered answer column. Although you should rely principally on your recollection, you can use the textbook if you need help. Check your answers by referring to the keys at the back of this study guide.

1 The Persistence of Individuality

CONCEPT   People behave differently because of their uniquely different personalities and backgrounds.

Answers

1. A key part of the supervisor's job is seeking to __(1)__ employees before deciding how to __(2)__ and lead them.

1. _____

2. _____

2. A person's __(3)__ is the total expression of the unique way he or she deals with life.

3. _____

3. Supervisors deal with employees who have brought their previous experiences to the job.

4. Each person is a distinct individual.

5. You need to know why people do the things they do before you can __(4)__ what they will do.

6. Although what each person may do will differ, the underlying __(5)__ for doing anything fall into basic categories (motives, needs, or drives).

4. _____

5. _____

2 ▶ A Powerful Pattern of Motivation

CONCEPT   Individuals strive to satisfy a hierarchy of five basic needs.

1. Maslow identified __(6)__ basic needs, which are best seen as a __(7)__ with the most basic one coming first and the most sophisticated one last (see text Figure 9-1).
   a. Need to be alive and stay alive: __(8)__ need.
   b. Need to feel safe: safety need.
   c. Need to be social: social need.
   d. Need to feel worthy and respected: __(9)__ need.
   e. Need to do the work we like: __(10)__ need.

2. The most powerful employee needs are the one or ones that have not been __(11)__.

6. _____

7. _____

8. _____

9. _____

10. _____

11. _____

3 ▶ Satisfaction and Dissatisfaction

CONCEPT   Supervisors are key forces in providing employees with need satisfaction.

1. A job can often __(12)__ the first two basic needs; a good __(13)__ can help fulfill the other three basic needs:
   a. Social needs can be satisfied by showing direct care and concern for __(14)__.
   b. Esteem needs are met by showing workers that their work is __(15)__.
   c. The desire to do worthwhile work is achieved by assigning tasks that stretch an employee's __(16)__ while drawing on her or his aptitude and training.

2. Herzberg distinguished between satisfaction and __(17)__ in the following ways (see text Figure 9-2):
   a. Satisfaction comes from truly __(18)__ factors such as interesting and challenging work, utilization of one's capabilities, opportunity to do something meaningful, etc.
   b. Dissatisfaction occurs when the following factors are not present __(19)__: good pay, adequate holidays, long enough vacations, paid insurance, etc.

12. _____

13. _____

14. _____

15. _____

16. _____

17. _____

18. _____

19. _____

3. Responsibility for removing dissatisfaction and increasing satisfaction is one that is shared by the supervisor and the __(20)__.

20. _____

4 ▶ *Achievement, Expectancy, and Equity*

CONCEPT Employee performance is greatly influenced by the workers' opportunities for personal achievement, their expectancy of what the job will provide, and their desire for equity in the workplace.

1. According to David McClelland, people have varying degrees of drive toward achievement, power, and affiliation.

   a. Achievement-motivated people thrive on pursuing and __(21)__. They

   21. _____

   (1) Like to be able to __(22)__ the situations they are involved in.

   22. _____

   (2) Take __(23)__ risks but not great chances.

   23. _____

   (3) Like to get immediate __(24)__ on how they have done.

   24. _____

   (4) Tend to be preoccupied with a __(25)__ towards the job to be done.

   25. _____

   b. __(26)__-motivated individuals see almost every situation as an opportunity to seize control or dominate others. They

   26. _____

   (1) Love to __(27)__ others.

   27. _____

   (2) Like to change situations __(28)__ it is needed.

   28. _____

   (3) Are willing to __(29)__ themselves when a decision needs to be made.

   29. _____

   c. Affiliation-motivated people are usually __(30)__ and like to socialize with others.

   30. _____

   (1) This may distract them from their performance requirements.

   (2) They will usually respond to an appeal for __(31)__.

   31. _____

2. Employees often have the following questions about their job:

   a. Can I do what __(32)__ is asking me to do?

   32. _____

   b. If I do the job, will I be __(33)__?

   33. _____

   c. Will the reward I receive be __(34)__ to me?

   34. _____

3. Employees are very concerned about equity—the perception of __(35)__ involved in __(36)__ given by their supervisor.

   35. _____

   36. _____

   a. They will compare their rewards with the rewards received by others for their efforts.

b. If workers perceive that an __(37)__ exists, they are likely to withhold some of their __(38)__ (consciously or unconsciously) to bring a situation into better balance.

c. Supervisors must manage not only objective reality but also the perception of fairness in the mind of each employee.

37. _____

38. _____

5 ▶ Motivation in the Work Itself

CONCEPT   Employees can be greatly motivated by the design of their jobs and their involvement in work decisions.

1. Most work is originally designed to __(39)__ constraints such as
   a. Production specifications.
   b. Tool and machine requirements.
   c. __(40)__ sequences.
   d. Computer-assisted controls.
   e. __(41)__.

2. Many jobs need to be __(42)__ to take workers' psychological as well as __(43)__ needs into consideration.

3. Process re-engineering challenges old ways of doing things and encourages the removal of __(44)__ job steps.

4. __(45)__ is the authority of lower-level employees to examine problem situations and help __(46)__ them as they arise.
   a. Sometimes supervisors drag their feet because they fear loss of __(47)__.
   b. Sometimes employees try to exercise their new __(48)__ too fast.
   c. The motivational impact of empowerment is enormous and should not be overlooked by any supervisor.

5. Examples of people-centered job redesign include
   a. __(49)__, which extends the boundaries of the job.
   b. Job enrichment, which allows employees to perform job-related activities that are usually done by __(50)__.

6. Successful job redesign results in greater output per employee, improved quality of product or service, fewer absences, lower __(51)__, and greater __(52)__ from employees.

39. _____

40. _____

41. _____
42. _____
43. _____

44. _____

45. _____
46. _____

47. _____

48. _____

49. _____

50. _____

51. _____
52. _____

COMMENTARY ON SELF-APPRAISAL FROM THE TEXT

Motivational theory follows several avenues, and the approach in this chapter has been to simplify, rather than to be exhaustive or too theoretically precise. You should understand the generally accepted concepts reviewed in this self-appraisal but should be cautioned that human behavior is difficult to understand and to contend with in practice.

1. True. Supervisors who extend themselves to learn about all the factors that have influenced an employee's personality have laid the groundwork for a better understanding of that person's behavior and motivation.

2. True. If (see answer 1) a supervisor understands why a person acts the way he or she does, this greatly improves the possibility of predicting behavior—reactions and responses—to given circumstances. It does not, of course, guarantee that these predictions will be accurate, but they will be better than those based on no knowledge or understanding of the individual.

3. False. The most fundamental need is a physiological one—for survival. Self-actualization is the most esoteric (and psychological) need—and is most often at the top of an individual's priorities.

4. False. Maslow has shown, rather persuasively, that the needs of most human beings can best be understood and interpreted when arranged in a hierarchical pattern.

5. True. The temptation is to think that the appeal should be made to the next highest level; reason would show that the more basic, unsatisfied lower-level need has a stronger appeal.

6. True. Maslow characterized survival and security needs as physiological needs and social, esteem, and self-actualization needs as psychological needs.

7. True. Herzberg's reasoning is that satisfaction of lower-level needs (and social needs) in the workplace is taken for granted by employees in affluent nations, and thus does not motivate. The two higher-level needs remain as the most difficult to satisfy in the workplace, and thus become strong motivators.

8. True. Because of the expectations of satisfaction, the absence of job conditions that satisfy these lower-level needs invites dissatisfaction—not motivation—when not satisfied. There is little drive to satisfy these needs by working harder. Dissatisfied employees will malinger, become absent, or look elsewhere for employment.

9. True. It is important to grasp this connection. Herzberg's satisfiers and motivators are all aimed at actions that improve the quality of work life for an employee. He did not use that language, but that is what his two-factor theory has led to.

10. True. Expectancy has three elements: (a) expectancy of being able to perform as requested, (b) expectancy of a reward for performing that way, and (c) the value placed upon the reward as compared with the effort involved. If the estimate of any of these three elements is low, then the effort will not be made.

11. True. Achievement-motivated people often have low affiliation needs and are not concerned about whether their efforts please others. Affiliation-motivated people are more interested in socializing and developing close relationships than in the outcome of their work efforts. The differences in motivational needs between the two make for workplace problems.

12. False. Employees look beyond their own personal rewards when determining whether they are being treated equitably. This comparison will include looking at what similar workers receive for similar work.

13. True. Job enrichment is a form of job redesign that increases employees' job satisfaction and provides them with opportunities for increased autonomy.

14. False. Contacts with users, customers, and clients are distinct features of the people-centered approach: this makes work more meaningful and also provides direct feedback (even if critical) from the work itself.

15. True. Herzberg's satisfiers and motivators and the people-centered approach to job redesign all imply greater participation and involvement on the part of the workers.

SELF-CHECK OF YOUR PROGRESS

Part A: COMPLETION An important term or phrase is needed to complete each of the following statements. Write the missing term in the space provided in the answer column.

Answers

1. A. H. Maslow taught that people are motivated to behavior by basic ____.

1. _____

2. Mary continues to work even though she doesn't need the money; she works just for the fun of being around other people. She is probably largely motivated by ____ needs.

2. _____

3. In seven years, Stephen has held five different jobs; he has continually searched for work that would be truly interesting and fulfilling. Stephen is probably largely motivated by ____ needs.

3. _____

4. A need is motivating only when it has not yet been ____.

4. _____

5. Barney lets all of his employees know that the reason the company provides such good facilities for workers is that the contribution of the workers is highly appreciated. Barney is trying to satisfy ____ needs.

5. _____

6. Wages and working conditions as described by Herzberg are called ____.

6. _____

7. ____ is an employee's perception of the fairness in the application of rewards to oneself and others for their efforts.

7. _____

8. The process of carefully restructuring a job to foster productivity and to appeal to the interest of the employees who carry it out is referred to as ____.

8. _____

9. Zelda has a high need for ____. One sign of this is her tendency to tell other people what to do even when she isn't officially in charge.

9. _____

10. David McClelland believes that the need for ____ is especially high among people who become managers.

10. _____

Part B: TRUE-FALSE   By writing T or F in the space provided, indicate whether each statement is true or false.

Answers

1. By and large, people's reactions at work are irrational.   1. ____

2. Supervisors should avoid job enlargement because it confuses most employees.   2. ____

3. Sally is a very conscientious employee who tries her best to work toward the goals of the meat-packing company that employs her. Such a worker is pretty unlikely to be influenced on the job by outside forces such as family and social life.   3. ____

4. According to early studies by A. H. Maslow, all humans have a certain need to be social, even at work.   4. ____

5. Higher-level needs, such as the need for esteem and the need to engage in activities that are interesting in themselves, rarely have any practical effect at work.   5. ____

6. A supervisor can do a lot to see that an employee's needs to be social, to be respected, and to do likable work are met.   6. ____

7. The employees in Roberto's file management department are probably highly satisfied because Roberto focuses his day-to-day relationships with them on compliance with company policies and procedures.   7. ____

8. According to Herzberg, Claude can expect considerable success from his plan to increase worker motivation by giving a small pay raise to all employees.   8. ____

9. Since supervisors often have little control over the factors that create dissatisfaction, their main motivational routes are through application of the factors that give satisfaction.   9. ____

10. Throughout her career, Karen has taken extreme risks that most people consider foolhardy. Karen probably has a high need for achievement as defined by David McClelland.   10. ____

Part C: MULTIPLE CHOICE   Choose the response that best completes each statement. Write the letter of the response in the space provided.

Answers

1. The human need that serves as the strongest motivator is
   a. The one that has not yet been satisfied.
   b. The one that is the highest in the needs hierarchy, that is, the self-actualization need.
   c. The one that comes first in the hierarchy, that is, the survival need.
   d. The one that is the easiest to satisfy in a given situation.   1. ____

2. Frank's job pays a good wage, and he feels safe and secure at work and at home. Early studies of A. H. Maslow would predict that Frank would be most motivated by
   a. Survival needs.
   b. Safety needs.
   c. Social needs.
   d. The desire for pay increases.   2. ____

3. According to the expectancy view, which of the following questions would most directly and generally affect an employee's motivation?
   a. "Does my supervisor have any chance of being promoted?"
   b. "Do my coworkers respect me and like me?"
   c. "Can I really do the work that my supervisor is asking me to do?"
   d. "Can I stick on this job long enough to get any retirement pay?"   3. ____

4. According to Herzberg, adequate paid holidays and vacations can be expected to
   a. Provide real worker satisfaction.
   b. Serve as strong motivators toward good performance.
   c. Help prevent employee dissatisfaction.
   d. Make employees less concerned with whether the work itself is interesting.   4. ____
5. Adrienne tells an employee, "I would like your ideas on how to do this job more effectively." She is trying to create
   a. Employee empowerment.
   b. Process-centered redesign.
   c. Employee safety standards.
   d. None of the above.   5. ____
6. Which of the following workers is probably motivated largely by the need for achievement?
   a. Barbara, who always insists on doing her work in her own way in spite of instructions to the contrary.
   b. Galen, who sometimes falls behind schedule because he likes to talk with his coworkers.
   c. Steve, who doesn't care what anyone else—including his supervisor—thinks about his work quality.
   d. Carol, who gets a little upset if she doesn't find out right away whether her work quality is good or bad.   6. ____
7. Employee motivation is influenced by
   a. The degree to which an individual seeks achievement, affiliation, or power.
   b. The expectancy of rewards and the value placed on them.
   c. The desire to receive equitable treatment at work.
   d. All of the above.   7. ____
8. When Jamal wonders whether management will recognize and reward his work, he is
   a. Exhibiting power motivation.
   b. Concerned with expectancy of what the job will provide.
   c. Making a case for employee empowerment.
   d. Exhibiting his personality.   8. ____
9. People-centered job design differs from process-centered job design because it is concerned with
   a. Computer-assisted control.
   b. Tool and machine requirements.
   c. Process-flow sequences.
   d. Making the work more satisfying to human beings.   9. ____
10. Each of the following is one of the critical factors of job design identified by AT&T experts except
   a. Work space layout.
   b. A variety of tasks and skills.
   c. Regular contact with users.
   d. A chance for self-development.   10. ____

10 Leadership Skills, Styles, and Qualities

LEARNING OBJECTIVES

After studying this chapter, you should be able to

1. Describe the essential skills of leadership.

2. Explain the relationship between leadership and motivation, and differentiate between the assumptions of Theory X and Theory Y.

3. Recognize the various leadership styles, explain the benefits and prerequisites of a participative approach, and identify the two concerns of the Managerial Grid©.

4. Discuss the factors a leader should consider when selecting a leadership style, and explain two models for choosing a style on a situational basis.

5. Discuss the leader's responsibility for being an effective follower, actions for helping employees become self-leaders, and the role of substitutes for leadership.

CHAPTER STUDY GUIDE OUTLINES

Based on your study of the text chapter and/or your instructor's lesson presentation, complete the following outlines by supplying the correct answers for the numbered spaces. Some answers require more than one word to complete. Write the answers in the numbered answer column. Although you should rely principally on your recollection, you can use the textbook if you need help. Check your answers by referring to the keys at the back of this study guide.

▶ Leadership Defined

CONCEPT   Given certain characteristics, a supervisor may acquire and develop the skills required for effective leadership.

Answers

1. __(1)__ is the process of influencing and supporting others to follow you and to do willingly the things that need to be done.

   a. The actions the leader requests should be __(2)__, relevant, and ethical.

   b. Supervisors' requests should be appropriate actions that advance the department towards its goals of __(3)__, quality, service, and __(4)__.

1. _____

2. _____

3. _____

4. _____

c. Effective leaders get willing and enthusiastic __(5)__ from their employees.

d. As employees develop their __(6)__ and experience, they should begin to accept some of the __(7)__ for seeing what needs to be done.

2. Most leaders must learn their skills (see Superscope, Important Leadership Traits).

3. While a good personality helps, fair play, interest in others, good decisions, and honest character will help make you a __(8)__ leader.

4. __(9)__ is a leadership characteristic that can help motivate workers into early and sustained action.

a. Charismatic leaders tend to have expertise, be self-confident, take __(10)__ risks, and express high performance expectations for others.

b. Their language, behavior, and personal __(11)__ seem to inspire others around them.

5. Leaders must master the skills of __(12)__, influence, and rapport.

5. _____

6. _____

7. _____

8. _____

9. _____

10. _____

11. _____

12. _____

2 ▶ *Leadership and Motivation*

CONCEPT   Leadership relies upon providing direction that satisfies the motivational needs of others, and the direction chosen reflects a supervisor's assumptions about these needs.

1. __(13)__ and leadership are related (see text Figure 10-1).

a. Motivation is the power to satisfy __(14)__.

b. Leaders don't __(15)__; rather, they provide satisfaction or the means of satisfaction for the needs of others by

(1) First __(16)__ the needs of others.

(2) Then applying persuasion and influence to demonstrate that __(17)__ will come from following the leader's views.

c. People can be motivated without leadership, but __(18)__ cannot be successful without motivated followers.

2. According to Douglas McGregor, two theories about human nature and behavior, (__(19)__ and Theory Y), characterize current management thinking.

a. Theory X, the traditional management philosophy, implicitly assumes people

(1) __(20)__ work and will avoid it if possible.

13. _____

14. _____

15. _____

16. _____

17. _____

18. _____

19. _____

20. _____

    (2) Must be __(21)__, controlled, directed, or threatened to get adequate effort.

21. _____

    (3) Prefer to be directed, avoid __(22)__, have little ambition, and want security most.

22. _____

  b. __(23)__, based on recent and emerging knowledge of human behavior, assumes

23. _____

    (1) Effort at work is as __(24)__ as play or rest.

24. _____

    (2) People will exercise __(25)__ in the service of objectives to which they are __(26)__.

25. _____

26. _____

    (3) Commitment to objectives depends on the __(27)__ associated with their __(28)__.

27. _____

28. _____

    (4) Under proper conditions, people accept and seek __(29)__.

29. _____

    (5) Organizational __(30)__ skills are widely distributed among men and women.

30. _____

    (6) At present, the intellectual potentials of people at work are only partially being __(31)__.

31. _____

  c. McGregor believes the ability to help people discover goals consistent with those of the organization is the essence of __(32)__ (Theory Y).

32. _____

  d. If your assumptions about the motivations of others are correct, your leadership problems should be __(33)__.

33. _____

▶ Leadership Styles and Concepts

    CONCEPT   Leadership styles range widely from a job- or task-centered orientation to a people- or relationship-centered one, with many other combinations. A participative style has special merit for consideration.

1. Style of leadership refers to the __(34)__ a supervisor uses in trying to direct, activate, or otherwise provide a motivational atmosphere for employees. It includes leadership traits, skills, attitudes, and behaviors that employees perceive their supervisor to have and consistently use.

34. _____

2. An autocratic or __(35)__ is one in which the leader sets goals, makes decisions, gives orders, and demands obedience.

35. _____

  a. This is the Theory X approach.

  b. It can produce __(36)__ and may be appropriate when time is tight or a crisis is present.

36. _____

  c. In the long run, employee commitment suffers, and __(37)__ problems may arise.

37. _____

3. A democratic or consultative style is one in which the leader presents problems, consults with relevant individuals, or solicits ideas from those with expertise and interest before making a __(38)__.

38. _____

a. With this style, there is lots of involvement and strong teamwork—the Japanese call this __(39)__ management.

39. _____

b. Critics say it leads to __(40)__ compromises.

40. _____

4. The __(41)__ leadership style relies on the employee's sense of responsibility in good judgment and the supervisor's capacity to "let go" of some authority.

41. _____

a. It is highly consistent with the need to __(42)__ employees (see Chapter 9) and the assumptions of Theory Y.

42. _____

b. True participation gives one or more employees the right to explore problems, gather information, make decisions, and __(43)__ them.

43. _____

c. The positive result is employees are mentally and emotionally __(44)__ to its success.

44. _____

d. Not all employees are __(45)__ ready for it, and it can be threatening to a supervisor's desire to be in __(46)__.

45. _____

46. _____

e. Conditions that should be in place to help the participative approach succeed include

(1) Adequate __(47)__ to consult with employees.

47. _____

(2) The __(48)__ of allowing participation must exceed the cost.

48. _____

(3) The issue must be sufficiently __(49)__ to engage the workers' minds and imaginations.

49. _____

(4) The problem must be within the supervisor's area of job freedom.

(5) Not all problems lend themselves to the participative approach, and the supervisor and __(50)__ must understand this.

50. _____

5. Examples of formal programs that encourage employee participation include

a. __(51)__ systems, which invite individual employees to submit recommendations for work improvements.

51. _____

b. Quality circles and __(52)__ programs, which involve formal training and problem solving, group decision making, and statistical techniques to encourage employees to continuously search for improvements in their operations.

52. _____

c. Employee __(53)__ plans, also called employee stock ownership plans (ESOPs), which allow employees to purchase shares of common stock in the company, thereby becoming part owners.

6. The __(54)__ helps supervisors assess their personal leadership approach (see text Figure 10-2). The goal is a leader with a high concern for people and production (grid location 9,9).

53. _____

54. _____

4 ▶ Selecting an Appropriate Style

CONCEPT   Leadership styles should be selected with a keen sensitivity to the individuals and circumstances involved.

1. __(55)__ leadership models maintain that leaders need to assess several key factors before making a decision on which style to adopt, in contrast to the Managerial Grid©, which implies that the need for leadership should always be fully balanced between all-out concerns for both people and production.

55. _____

2. The __(56)__ model developed by Fiedler is an example of the situational approach. It identifies three critical factors:

56. _____

a. The quality of __(57)__ relations.

b. The level of __(58)__ in the job in terms of how carefully procedures and specifications must be followed.

57. _____
58. _____

c. The amount of real __(59)__ invested in the supervisor by her or his superiors.

59. _____

d. The model relates this assessment to research results showing whether a task-centered (authoritative) or people-centered (democratic or participative) style is called for.

3. An autocratic, authoritative (task-centered) style works best in situations where the supervisor has lots of real power; the process requires strong control and rapport is good, and in situations where just the opposite conditions prevail. A __(60)__ (people-centered) style is best where the supervisor's authority hasn't been clearly spelled out or acknowledged, where the process and procedures are somewhat flexible, and where the rapport is only average (see text Figure 10-3).

60. _____

4. The situational style opens the opportunity to select a style most suitable for the individuals and __(61)__ involved.

61. _____

a. Leadership style may be best thought of as a continuum from complete authority to nearly complete freedom (see text Figure 10-4).

5. Hersey's and Blanchard's situational (or __(62)__) model of leadership suggests employees vary in two ways, their task-specific __(63)__ and their motivation to perform (__(64)__). This can be thought of as task-related maturity.

62. _____

63. _____

64. _____

a. Supervisors can help develop task-related maturity by

(1) Providing appropriate guidance and feedback.

(2) Offering a variety of __(65)__.

(3) __(66)__ the rewards for cooperative behavior.

65. _____

66. _____

b. Any work group may have a mixture of members who are at different levels of task-related maturity.

c. The Hersey/Blanchard model suggests supervisors adapt their approach to fit the developmental stage of each employee.

(1) Use a __(67)__ style at low levels.

(2) More __(68)__ styles at intermediate levels.

(3) A __(69)__ style for employees at high levels of development.

67. _____

68. _____

69. _____

d. The key to this model is in analyzing each employee's stage of development, working with them to move upward, and matching your style to fit their current needs.

6. There will be times when you should deviate from the prescriptions of the situational models. For example, autocratic leadership may work best in __(70)__ situations.

70. _____

5 ▸ Leaders and Followers

CONCEPT Supervisors must consider both themselves and their employees as followers and also acknowledge there are substitutes for effective leadership.

1. Supervisors should remember they are both leaders and followers.

a. A supervisor's reputation depends not only on being an effective leader, but also being a loyal supporter of his or her boss.

b. An effective __(71)__ is also an important role and needs to be balanced with the leadership role.

71. _____

2. Good supervisors will consider the opportunity to be a "superleader" for their employees. According to Manz and Sims, this is a person who
   a. Places high priority on unleashing and expanding the __(72)__ of subordinates.

   b. Encourages employees to practice __(73)__ skills.

   c. Creates __(74)__ situations.

3. It is important to develop plans for the __(75)__ of the department when the supervisor is not available.
   a. Create self-leading employees.

   b. __(76)__ for leadership.

     (1) Less direction is needed if there is strong subordinate experience, clear policies and rules, or a __(77)__ work group with a __(78)__ attitude.

     (2) Intrinsically satisfying tasks, employees with a professional orientation, and individuals with a high need for __(79)__.

4. The real lesson—don't cling to a __(80)__ definition of your leadership.

5. Leaders can't always be __(81)__ with the people they supervise.
   a. Many decisions won't __(82)__ everyone.

   b. Supervisors need to be satisfied that their leadership has been __(83)__, considerate, and __(84)__.

72. _____

73. _____

74. _____

75. _____

76. _____

77. _____

78. _____

79. _____

80. _____

81. _____

82. _____

83. _____

84. _____

COMMENTARY ON SELF-APPRAISAL FROM THE TEXT

This exercise is a straightforward review of terms and concepts. While the incentive for trying the self-appraisal is to assess your leadership aptitude, this is not in any valid way a measure of leadership potential. It is, instead, a measure of your understanding of leadership terms and concepts. This is an essential requirement for studying leadership styles and skills and for acquiring and developing them through practice and experience.

1. Disagree. Leadership power comes from expert knowledge and personal charisma as well as from formal position power.

2. Disagree. Many good leaders do not have a particularly strong charisma; they rely on leadership skills for their effectiveness.

3. Agree. Leadership, for supervisors at any rate, should be confined to legitimate actions and goals.

4. Agree. Read McGregor's statement about the essence of leadership under Concept 2.

5. Disagree. Theory X assumptions breed autocratic leaders; Theory Y induces participative leadership.

6. Agree. Refer to Theory X and Theory Y in Concept 2.

7. Agree. See Figure 10-4 in the text.

8. Agree. See Concept 4 and text Figure 10-3.

9. Disagree. The two axes of the Managerial Grid© are a concern for people and a concern for production. See Figure 10-2 in the text.

10. Disagree. It is emotional maturity, not chronological age, upon which the life-cycle concept of leadership turns.

11. Disagree. There are many instances when there is not time for allowing employee participation in decisions.

12. Disagree. Autocratic leadership is, by far, the best style to use in an emergency.

13. Agree. Hersey's and Blanchard's situational (or life-cycle) model of leadership emphasizes that effective supervisors adapt their leadership style to the competence and commitment of their employees.

14. Agree. See Concept 5.

15. Disagree. Unfortunately, good leadership and widespread popularity among employees do not necessarily go hand in hand. There are too many decisions that a supervisor must render that are unpopular with one or another segment of employees.

SELF-CHECK OF YOUR PROGRESS

Part A: COMPLETION An important term or phrase is needed to complete each of the following statements. Write the missing term in the space provided in the answer column.

Answers

1. It is essential to determine the amount of real authority the supervisor's superiors have allowed him or her, according to the ____ model.

1. _____

2. A supervisor who can persuade her or his employees to follow her or his instructions willingly has developed ____.

2. _____

3. Motivation arises out of an individual's desire to meet a ____.

3. _____

4. Asking an employee's opinion before making a decision is an example of ____.

4. _____

5. The ____ allows a supervisor to choose an approach ranging from demanding obedience to allowing complete freedom.

5. _____

6. The ____ leadership style relies on the employee's sense of responsibility, judgement, and the supervisor's ability to let go of some authority.

6. _____

7. Supervisors' skill at ____ relies both on rational development of arguments and on convincing presentation of them.

7. _____

8. The ratio between concern for people and concern for production can be shown on the ____.

8. _____

9. Theory ____ assumes that a supervisor will integrate employee needs with departmental needs.

9. _____

10. Supervisors who place a high priority on win–win relationships and developing the skills of employees to manage themselves and engage in self-leadership are referred to as ____.

10. _____

Part B: TRUE-FALSE   By writing T or F in the space provided, indicate whether each statement is true or false.

Answers

1. Leadership requires a supervisor to use persuasion, control, and rapport with their employees.

1. _____

2. The first requirement of a good leader is to develop rapport with others.

2. _____

3. The motivational needs of all workers on an assembly line are the same.

3. _____

4. A supervisor who knows the job has developed a good foundation for good leadership.

4. _____

5. The autocratic approach to leading people emphasizes the job to be done and not the people involved.

5. _____

6. The authoritative approach is most effective when conditions are very unfavorable but will not work when conditions are favorable.

6. _____

7. The most effective leaders use different kinds of leadership, depending on the situation and the people involved.

7. _____

8. The maturing of a new department can be compared with the natural stages of the human life cycle.

8. _____

9. Supervisors who place more emphasis on the employees they supervise than on a high rate of production usually get better production results.

9. _____

10. Theory X assumes that a worker has an inherent dislike of work and will avoid it if possible.

10. _____

Part C: MULTIPLE CHOICE   Choose the response that best completes each statement. Write the letter of the response in the space provided.

Answers

1. Ruth wants to become a good leader. Which of the following statements will most help her develop her leadership skills?
   a. Forget it—leaders are born, not made.
   b. Master skills of persuasion, influence, and rapport.
   c. Pick one leadership style and stick with it.
   d. Provide the necessary motivation to get employees to meet your needs.

1. _____

2. Each of the following assumptions about Theory Y and the average human being is correct except
   a. Currently his or her potential is only partially realized.
   b. Prefers to be directed.
   c. The expenditure of effort at work is as natural as play or rest.
   d. Will accept and seek responsibility.

2. _____

3. Jeff plans to use the Japanese consensus style of leadership. He should be aware of the fact that
   a. It works best with emergency decisions.
   b. It is less effective with other ethnic and minority employees.
   c. It is similar to the consultative leadership style.
   d. Theory X employees disrupt the process.

3. _____

4. The situational leadership style is based on the premise
   a. That the task to be done determines the leadership style needed.
   b. That the type of leadership needed is based on the relationship among three key factors.
   c. That times have changed and autocratic leadership is no longer acceptable.
   d. That situations can be manipulated to take advantage of your management style.

4. _____

5. Rapport, job precision, and supervisory power are important considerations of which of the following leadership styles?
   a. Contingency.
   b. Participative.
   c. Directive.
   d. Democratic.   5. ____

6. Sig is trying to apply the principles of the Managerial Grid© to her leadership style. She should
   a. Place the greatest emphasis on concern for people.
   b. Place the greatest emphasis on concern for production.
   c. Assume that concern for production and people are on a continuum.
   d. Place the highest emphasis on concern for both people and production.   6. ____

7. The following list of leadership styles represents a continuum from least employee freedom to most employee freedom.
   a. Autocratic, democratic, participative.
   b. Participative, autocratic, democratic.
   c. Democratic, participative, autocratic.
   d. Participative, democratic, autocratic.   7. ____

8. According to the life-cycle theory of leadership, if Betty is managing a newly formed department, it will probably need
   a. An autocratic style.
   b. A democratic style.
   c. A contingency style.
   d. A participative style.   8. ____

9. One of your employees, Clete, has an aggressive, cooperative personality. The style of leadership that is likely to be the least effective is
   a. Democratic.
   b. Free-rein.
   c. Autocratic.
   d. All the styles will have the same level of effectiveness.   9. ____

10. A supervisor's use of the situational or life-cycle model of leadership will be most successful if the supervisor
    a. Takes time to analyze each employee's stage of development.
    b. Works with employees to move them upward.
    c. Matches leadership style to fit current employee needs.
    d. Hires only self-directed employees.   10. ____

CHAPTER 11 Effective Employee Communication

LEARNING OBJECTIVES

After studying this chapter, you should be able to

1. Explain the process of communication, including the major steps essential for its success.

2. Choose appropriate spoken and written methods for communicating with individuals and groups of employees.

3. Assess the quality of your nonverbal communication skills and identify needed changes.

4. List the major communication guidelines that help create positive working relationships.

5. Use your knowledge of the communication process to make orders and instructions more acceptable to employees.

CHAPTER STUDY GUIDE OUTLINES

Based on your study of the text chapter and/or your instructor's lesson presentation, complete the following outlines by supplying the correct answers for the numbered spaces. Some answers require more than one word to complete. Write the answers in the numbered answer column. Although you should rely principally on your recollection, you can use the textbook if you need help. Check your answers by referring to the keys at the back of this study guide.

▶ 1 The Communication Process

CONCEPT Employee communication is a continuous process involving skillful sending and receiving of messages.

Answers

1. Communication is the process of passing __(1)__ and understanding from one person to another. It includes

   a. Employee communications, communications between supervisors, and communications with managers.

   b. Mechanical and electronic means of transmitting and receiving information.

1. _____

2. To help employees understand what the supervisors mean, supervisors should
   a. __(2)__ what they say.
   b. Ask the employees to repeat what the supervisors have said.
   c. Get the employees to ask questions.
   d. Be specific and avoid unclear meanings in words.

3. Communication activates an organization by providing the __(3)__ between plans and actions.

4. A supervisor's __(4)__ is measured in part by how the supervisor passes information on to others.

5. The communication process enables an idea in one person's mind to be transmitted, understood, and acted on by another person (see text Figure 11-1). It requires
   a. Having rapport with employees.
   b. Being __(5)__ to how others perceive ideas and information.
   c. Minimizing distracting noise.
   d. Being skilled in the spoken and written word and also nonverbal communication.
   e. Being skilled at receiving communications, including feedback and questions.

6. __(6)__ communication means that communication occurs in three ways:
   a. A supervisor communicates downward to employees, communicates upward to managers, and receives upward communication from employees.
   b. A supervisor communicates __(7)__ with other supervisors.
   c. A supervisor communicates with "outside" sources like vendors and customers.

7. __(8)__ is the process of gathering data on a supervisor's skills, abilities, and style from his or her manager, peers, subordinates, and even customers.
   a. The results are compared with the organizational norms for a good supervisor, the supervisor's perceptions, and data from earlier surveys.
   b. The process works best when it is voluntary and based on anonymous responses.
   c. The result is feedback, both positive and negative, that can aid in supervisory development.

2. _____

3. _____

4. _____

5. _____

6. _____

7. _____

8. _____

2 ► *Methods of Communication*

CONCEPT   Effective supervisors select their communication methods on the basis of careful analysis of situational factors.

1. Selection of a communication method depends on the __(9)__ as well as on your objectives.

   a. Length, permanency, informality, personal impact, and single-employee or group communications are all factors that affect the method selected.

   b. A need or interest in control, a need for privacy, and a need for opening up communications to initiate ideas also affect the method selected.

2. Custom tailoring of person-to-person communication is important. It is a way of recognizing that the people you are communicating with are unique.

   a. __(10)__ communication allows you and your receiver to be immediately aware of the conditions under which the message is shared. Methods include

      (1) __(11)__: suitable for day-to-day liaison, directions, exchange of information, progress reviews, discipline, and the maintenance of effective personal relations.

      (2) Planned __(12)__: appropriate for regular appraisal review, recurring joint work sessions, and so forth. These are most effective when you come prepared, bring adequate data, and when interruptions are limited.

      (3) __(13)__: for quick checkups and for imparting or receiving information. Remember, your telephone personality can contradict your real self. Try to follow up routine calls with occasional personal notes.

   b. __(14)__ communication should be used when the situation is formal, official, or long term; when it is necessary to correct previous written communication; or when the situation affects several people in related ways.

      (1) Interoffice memos—for recording informal inquiries or replies.

9. _____

10. _____

11. _____

12. _____

13. _____

14. _____

(2) Letters—usually addressed to an individual and often formal in tone; used for official notices, formally recorded statements, and lengthy communications.

(3) __(15)__: more impersonal and more formal than a letter; used to convey information, analyses, and recommendations.

15. _____

3. Communicating with groups of employees involves spoken and written communication.

   a. Spoken—informal staff meetings, planned conferences, and __(16)__.

16. _____

   b. Written—bulletin-board notices, posters, exhibits, displays, and audio and visual aids.

4. Each communication situation has its own best method or combination of methods. Good supervisors

   a. Quickly __(17)__ the situation.

17. _____

   b. Know and use many methods of effective communication.

5. Pay attention to the __(18)__, but don't depend on it for accurate information and don't make a practice of leaking information to it.

18. _____

3 ▶ *Nonverbal Communication*

CONCEPT Nonverbal behaviors—actions, body language, and active listening—are vitally important communication skills.

1. Actions really do speak __(19)__ than words.

19. _____

2. Body language is nonverbal body or facial expressions that express to others what is really on your mind.

3. Listening requires good __(20)__, alert body posture, and the frequent use of __(21)__ encouragement; it should make up at least a third of your communications.

20. _____

21. _____

   a. Don't assume anything.

   b. Don't __(22)__.

22. _____

   c. Try to understand the need.

   d. Don't react too quickly.

4 ▶ *Communication Guidelines*

CONCEPT Effective communication helps to develop positive working relationships with both a supervisor's boss and employees.

1. Act in good faith, build mutual confidence, welcome employee __(23)__, and have a receptive attitude.

23. _____

2. Accept responsibility to keep __(24)__ on matters of likely importance to employees.

24. _____

3. Never bluff or pass the buck when caught __(25)__ .

25. _____

4. Be aware of the common communication hazards for supervisors:
   a. Overcommunicating—talking too much and listening too little.
   b. Violating confidences.
   c. Expressing views on intensely __(26)__ matters like politics, religion, and social values.

26. _____

   d. Making comments with __(27)__ overtones or creating an offensive working environment.

27. _____

   e. Stepping on a person's ego—putting the person on the defensive.

5. Keep your boss informed on
   a. Progress toward __(28)__ goals and standards.

28. _____

   b. Matters that may cause controversy.
   c. Attitudes and morale.

5► Commands and Instructions

CONCEPT   Supervisors exercise their authority by issuing commands and giving instructions and directions.

1. Orders and instructions are the most direct, authority-based kinds of communication.
   a. Be sure employees understand what needs to be done.
   b. Be sure employees do it __(29)__ .

29. _____

   c. Be sure your order is the right one for the particular situation.
   d. Be __(30)__ about what the employee is to do and what kind of results you expect.

30. _____

   e. Select the right person to carry out your orders.
   f. Express __(31)__ in the person you select.

31. _____

   g. Repeat or rephrase your order for additional impact.
   h. Check regularly to see how things are going.

2. When an employee willfully refuses to work, analyze the __(32)__ before attempting to resolve it.

32. _____

   a. Don't fly off the handle; instead
      (1) Review your order's fairness, the selection of the __(33)__, and the probability you were understood.

33. _____

      (2) Find out what the employee __(34)__ to.

34. _____

      (3) The use of __(35)__ instead of orders gives workers a sense of freedom of action, creating a source of job satisfaction.

35. _____

3. There are ten guidelines for avoiding trouble when directing, ordering, assigning, or instructing:

    a. Don't make it a struggle for __(36)__ .

    b. Avoid a casual manner.

    c. Watch out for your words.

    d. Don't assume that the worker understands.

    e. Seek __(37)__ right away.

    f. Don't give too many __(38)__ .

    g. Provide just enough detail.

    h. Watch out for __(39)__ instructions.

    i. Carefully select the recipient.

    j. Above all, don't flaunt your __(40)__ .

36. _____

37. _____

38. _____

39. _____

40. _____

COMMENTARY ON SELF-APPRAISAL FROM THE TEXT

Although it may be difficult to "see" Karl's listening behaviors from the reports of the police who were interviewed, this self-appraisal provides an opportunity to think about some of the elements of effective listening. The real purpose, of course, is to encourage you to examine your own listening habits and anticipate the probable reactions of others to your own areas of strength and weakness. Karl apparently does some things well, while other behaviors could be improved. The rationale behind the scoring for each item is provided here.

1. Needs some improvement. It appears that when you are on Karl's "agenda," he is fully attentive, but at other times he does not completely focus his listening energies.

2. Bad practice. Especially in this area of work involving careful evidence gathering, rights of the accused, and intricate criminal laws, Karl needs to reserve judgment until all information has been presented. He is creating a poor model for his staff.

3. Needs some improvement. Although this doesn't necessarily imply Karl isn't listening carefully, any mannerism such as this can be distracting to the speaker.

4. Good practice. This indicates that Karl has high interest and a desire to learn about the subject in greater depth. It also encourages police officers to do their "homework" in advance or be prepared for rapid thinking while they are in the "hotseat."

5. Needs some improvement. Although this may not be as bad as the individual who totally avoids eye contact while listening, it is uncomfortable to endure continuous staring. A preferable behavior involves regular but short periods of eye contact.

6. Bad practice. Presumably Karl's intentions (good time management) are commendable, but the effect is to distract and likely even irritate other people in attendance.

7. Needs some improvement. Karl would probably argue that he is introducing useful historical examples that relate to the present case, and this may be true. However, if the stories serve only his own needs for reminiscing about the past, they may be detrimental to the systematic flow of thought required to think through a complex case. In that event, they should be minimized.

8. Needs some improvement. Presumably, Karl is simply attempting to shut out all visual distractions around him and focus his thoughts, which is commendable. At a minimum, however, he needs to explain this practice to the police officers making the report so they won't falsely conclude that he is just bored, tired, and so forth.

9. Good practice. Nonverbal actions are important supplements to the words used in spoken or written communication. They provide useful advance clues to what Karl is thinking and feeling.

10. Bad practice. This implies to speakers in a conversation that they are the least important item on Karl's priority list. Karl's (noncrisis) phone calls should be held, visitors could return later, and the mail could be opened between meetings.

SELF-CHECK OF YOUR PROGRESS

Part A: COMPLETION An important term or phrase is needed to complete each of the following statements. Write the missing term in the space provided in the answer column.

Answers

1. The ____ is the entire process that enables one person to receive, understand, and act on what is in another person's mind.

1. _____

2. Communication that moves up, down, and across an organization is called ____.

2. _____

3. A frown, scratching one's nose, and rolling one's eyes are examples of ____.

3. _____

4. Information provided during the communication process that verifies understanding or indicates dissent or agreement is ____.

4. _____

5. The most fundamental form of communication is the ____.

5. _____

6. A common error in calling a ____ is failing to consult with the participants.

6. _____

7. ____ are the manners or forms by which information is transmitted.

7. _____

8. ____ is a physical or emotional distraction that distorts or obstructs the transmission of a message.

8. _____

9. The informal communication network that employees use to convey information is the ____.

9. _____

10. ____ is the conscious process of securing information through listening and observing.

10. _____

Part B: TRUE-FALSE By writing T or F in the space provided, indicate whether each statement is true or false.

Answers

1. The communication process includes nonverbal messages that your face and body give to others.

1. ____

2. Good communication of plans makes acting on the plans possible.

2. ____

3. The method a supervisor uses to communicate to his or her employees depends on the employee and/or the situation.

3. ____

4. Listening to the grapevine can provide clues about what's going on.

4. ____

5. Body language may better indicate what a person really thinks than what is said.

5. ____

6. A supervisor's listening skill is less important than the employee's ability to communicate.

6. ____

7. Communication is most effective when you know a variety of ways to get your idea across to others.

7. ____

8. Orders and instructions are part of the communication process.

8. ____

9. It should never be necessary for a supervisor to repeat an order.

9. ____

10. A supervisor should punish an employee at once who willfully disobeys an order.

10. ____

Part C: MULTIPLE CHOICE Choose the response that best completes each statement. Write the letter of the response in the space provided.

1. Which of the following statements is least likely to be misunderstood?
   a. Speed up the machine a little bit.
   b. Type this as soon as possible.
   c. I think you're doing a pretty good job.
   d. You need to deliver this within the next two hours.

Answers

1. ____

2. Written communications are generally better than oral communications for which of the following purposes?
   a. Speed.
   b. Lengthy message.
   c. Informality.
   d. Personal impact.   2. ____

3. Each of the following statements concerning the grapevine is true except:
   a. Supervisors should occasionally leak information through the grapevine.
   b. It is most actively used in the absence of good communication.
   c. Grapevine information is often based on incomplete data.
   d. Employees get lots of information through the grapevine.   3. ____

4. An example of in/out communication is speaking to
   a. Employees.
   b. The boss.
   c. An informal group leader.
   d. Customers.   4. ____

5. Which of the following is least likely to happen when communication occurs with the entire department?
   a. It invites employee participation.
   b. It develops commitment.
   c. It allows the supervisor to control the flow of information.
   d. It helps build team spirit.   5. ____

6. One thing that is true about body language is that
   a. Facial expressions can be misinterpreted.
   b. It always tells others what is really on your mind.
   c. Once aware of your body language, these actions are easy to change.
   d. You are always conscious of your body movements.   6. ____

7. Phyllis has asked you about the company's new maternity-leave policy. You've heard about it but can't remember all the details. You should
   a. Send her to the human resources department.
   b. Give your best understanding concerning policy provisions.
   c. Have her check with other employees.
   d. Accept your responsibility for keeping informed and get the accurate information as soon as possible.   7. ____

8. In communicating orders and instructions, who is responsible for the message?
   a. The employee.
   b. The supervisor.
   c. The manager of the company.
   d. The human resources department.   8. ____

9. A supervisor's first responsibility in communicating instructions is to
   a. Put the instructions in writing.
   b. Make sure the employees follow instructions properly.
   c. Make sure the employees know what to do.
   d. Call a departmental meeting.   9. ____

10. Which of the following is the best approach in dealing with an employee who refuses to carry out an order?
    a. Demand that the work be done, or else!
    b. Take immediate punitive action.
    c. Find out what the employee objects to.
    d. Point out the appropriate rule in the employee handbook.   10. ____

CHAPTER 12 Appraisal of Employee Performance

LEARNING OBJECTIVES

After studying this chapter, you should be able to

1. Explain the main purposes and benefits of an employee performance appraisal.

2. Describe the kinds of factors that are evaluated and the formats used, suggest ways of reducing bias, and recognize the influence of the halo effect.

3. List the main steps in an appraisal interview and discuss techniques for making it more effective.

4. Discuss ways of handling sensitive problems that may arise during, or as result of, the appraisal interview.

5. Explain the legal implications of a performance appraisal, recognize its limited relationship to financial rewards, and identify a number of extenuating circumstances that may cause poor performance.

CHAPTER STUDY GUIDE OUTLINES

Based on your study of the text chapter and/or your instructor's lesson presentation, complete the following outlines by supplying the correct answers for the numbered spaces. Some answers require more than one word to complete. Write the answers in the numbered answer column. Although you should rely principally on your recollection, you can use the textbook if you need help. Check your answers by referring to the keys at the back of this study guide.

1 ▶ Purposes of Appraisal

CONCEPT   Employees have a right to know, and a desire to know, how well they are performing and how they can improve.

1. The four basic reasons for making a performance appraisal are

   Answers

   a. To encourage __(1)__ or to correct and discourage below-standard performance.

   1. _____

   b. To satisfy employees' curiosity about how they are doing.

   c. To provide an opportunity for developing employee skills.

   d. To provide a firm foundation for later judgments that concern an employee's __(2)__ .

   2. _____

2. Employees will not resist evaluation based on facts, especially if you're willing to change the ratings if an employee can show you're wrong.
3. Formal evaluation should occur __(3)__ a year; informal evaluation should occur routinely.
4. The relationship of performance-appraisal to job evaluation, compensation rates, and merit raises depends on __(4)__.
   a. Job evaluation—appraising the worth of a particular job—is not a performance-appraisal issue.
   b. Compensation—a __(5)__ decision—is not a performance appraisal issue.
   c. Merit raises—salary increases based on merit—are perceived by many employees as the __(6)__ of performance appraisal.
      (1) Most organizations try to __(7)__ performance-appraisal sessions from decisions regarding merit raises.
      (2) Supervisors should avoid stressing the relationship between pay raises and the appraisal process.

3. _____

4. _____

5. _____

6. _____

7. _____

▶ 2 *Factors and Format*

CONCEPT   Appraisals evaluate, in a systematic way, an individual's job-related traits and behavior as they affect performance.

1. __(8)__ have encouraged organizations to specify and monitor their performance-appraisal programs.
   a. Weighted graphic rating scales (see text Table 12-1)
      (1) List factors of performance and permit a range of evaluation.
      (2) Often also include a numerical weight for each factor.
   b. __(9)__ format
      (1) This format consists of a series of paired descriptive statements.
      (2) The evaluator is forced to choose between statements.
2. Appraisal judgments fall into two categories:
   a. Objective factors—hard facts and measurable results.
   b. __(10)__ factors—opinions, best when supported with documented incidents.

8. _____

9. _____

10. _____

3. Performance is compared with stated responsibilities and standards of a specific job.

a. __(11)__ your ratings to be sure you don't favor one employee or make unsupported judgments.

11. _____

b. Be sure you don't rate all employees too high or too low.

c. Remember that all employees can rate __(12)__ if they meet their stipulated responsibilities and standards.

12. _____

4. It is very helpful to document __(13)__ of employee performance; then you can use them to illustrate and support your ratings.

13. _____

5. The __(14)__ is the tendency to let one favorable or unfavorable incident color your entire judgment (see Superscope "The Downside of Appraisals").

14. _____

a. Halo-effect biases include recency, overemphasis, unforgivingness, prejudice, favoritism, grouping, indiscrimination, and stereotyping.

b. The halo effect can be minimized by rating all employees on a single factor before moving to the next factor.

6. At the core of all successful appraisal formats are clearly defined, and explicitly __(15)__, standards or expectations of employee performance on the job. Types of formats include

15. _____

a. __(16)__ .

16. _____

(1) Describes various levels of behavior expected of the employee (see text Figure 12-1).

(2) Provides greater objectivity.

(3) Tends to focus on the __(17)__ rather than the results.

17. _____

b. Trait format.

(1) Focuses on traits such as initiative and dependability.

(2) Is almost unavoidably subjective; is difficult to defend in __(18)__ .

18. _____

c. Results-oriented appraisal.

(1) This is based on __(19)__ principles.

19. _____

(2) Specific objectives with measurable results become the basis for future appraisal.

(3) It is difficult to implement for employees who rely heavily on supervisors to plan and control work.

3 ▶ *The Appraisal Interview*

       CONCEPT   The appraisal interview is a developmental exchange between supervisor and employee, aimed at reinforcing appropriate—or correcting unsatisfactory—performance.

1. Use the seven-step approach in conducting the appraisal interview.
   a. Prepare the employee to come to the meeting expecting to compare notes.
   b. Compare __(20)__ with specific targets.   20. _____
   c. Give adequate credit for what has been accomplished.
   d. Emphasize where, how, and why __(21)__ is needed.   21. _____
   e. Stick to a mutual explanation of the __(22)__ and   22. _____
      their implications.
      (1) Share __(23)__ where appropriate.   23. _____
      (2) Never compare the employee with a third party.
   f. Agree on specific targets to meet in the period ahead.
   g. Review what __(24)__ can do to be of help.   24. _____
2. Conduct the interview in __(25)__ and allow adequate   25. _____
   time to complete the process.
3. __(26)__ unfavorable comments between favorable   26. _____
   comments (see text Figure 12-2).
4. Give the employee an opportunity to respond to your appraisal.
   a. Listen without interruption to discover underlying problems.
   b. Don't get angry.
5. Never discuss one employee's rating with another employee.

4 ▶ *Special Considerations*

       CONCEPT   Supervisors must be prepared to handle a variety of sensitive issues that may arise from the appraisal.

1. __(27)__ your reasoning, so that you will be prepared   27. _____
   to respond to charges of bias or favoritism.
2. Acknowledge top performances with __(28)__.   28. _____
3. Focus on improving the performance of poor performers.
   a. Be firm, be specific, and don't rub it in.
   b. End the discussion with a summary of satisfactory as well as unsatisfactory performance.
4. Acknowledge any real problems you have __(29)__   29. _____
   good performance, but don't oversympathize.

5. __(30)__ new employees as soon as a problem arises.

    a. Determine the cause of the problem.

    b. Document the appraisal in the employee's file.

6. In self-appraisal systems, employees are asked to evaluate their own __(31)__.

    a. They are given the criteria and performance standards, and then asked to complete rating forms.

    b. Most employees respond in __(32)__ ways; often they are more critical of themselves than their supervisor would have been.

    c. If self-appraisal is successful, it may help to eliminate one of the most frustrating of all supervisory tasks.

30. _____

31. _____

32. _____

▶5 *Legal and Financial Aspects*

CONCEPT   The appraisal represents a critical, legal communication to an employee and should be supported by objective reasoning and documentable evidence.

1. There are several legal implications of performance appraisal.

    a. __(33)__ pay for equal work.

    b. Absence of __(34)__ based on age, gender, religion, race, color, or national origin.

    c. __(35)__ of the physical and mental needs of the disabled and of Vietnam-era veterans.

    d. Equal employment opportunities.

2. To comply with legal requirements, the supervisor should try to

    a. Base the appraisal on the __(36)__ that the employee is expected to do.

    b. Be cautious in making subjective judgments.

    c. Stick to facts that can be documented.

    d. Do everything possible to avoid even the appearance of prejudice or discrimination.

3. It may be unwise to keep a __(37)__ record of the appraisal if you have developed a rapport during the interview, which might be destroyed by putting a summary of your critical comments in writing.

4. It is important to keep a written record of appraisal if you expect that __(38)__ may not be forthcoming.

5. Critical incidents should be collected in the employee's official file.

33. _____

34. _____

35. _____

36. _____

37. _____

30. _____

6. __(39)__, the concept used for evaluating the worth of widely dissimilar jobs, is only peripherally related to performance appraisal.

7. Many factors contribute to unsatisfactory employee performance.
   a. Workers may be assigned to work that doesn't match their __(40)__.
   b. Employees may not have received proper training.
   c. Workers may be victims of pressures from the __(41)__.
   d. Individuals may not be physically or emotionally up to the job requirements.
   e. Supervisors may be at fault.
   f. There may be problems with the __(42)__ systems.

39. _____

40. _____

41. _____

42. _____

COMMENTARY ON SELF-APPRAISAL FROM THE TEXT

This self-appraisal enables you to verify how well you understand the concepts and terminology in the chapter, as well as to think about how others might evaluate your performance in the appraising role. Backup for answers to items 1 to 3 is found in section 1 of the chapter; for items 4 to 6 in section 2; for items 7 to 9 in section 3; for items 10 to 12 in section 4; and for items 13 to 15 in section 5.

SELF-CHECK OF YOUR PROGRESS

Part A: COMPLETION   An important term or phrase is needed to complete each of the following statements. Write the missing term in the space provided in the answer column.

Answers

1. A meeting between a supervisor and an employee to evaluate the employee's performance is a(n) ____ interview.

1. _____

2. A(n) ____ is a specific action on the part of an employee that represents the overall quality of an employee's work or attitude.

2. _____

3. Employee action taken to restore their self-image and regain their self-esteem after receiving criticism during an appraisal is referred to as ____.

3. _____

4. ____ is a systematic technique for determining the worth of a job compared with other jobs in an organization.

4. _____

5. A formal, systematic evaluation of how well a person is performing his or her work is called a(n) ____.

5. _____

6. ____ for a particular job is the result of a job-pricing decision.

6. _____

7. A performance rating system based on a series of paired descriptive statements is an example of the ____ format.

7. _____

8. Evaluations based on measurable results are based on ____ factors.

    8. _____

9. An employee who is highly motivated is a good candidate for the ____ approach to job performance.

    9. _____

10. ____ is a job evaluation technique used to evaluate the worth of widely dissimilar jobs.

    10. _____

Part B: TRUE-FALSE By writing T or F in the space provided, indicate whether each statement is true or false.

Answers

1. A behaviorally anchored rating scale (BARS) is an appraisal process that should be avoided because it is very subjective.

    1. ____

2. Employees resent being evaluated by their supervisors.

    2. ____

3. One objective of a performance appraisal is to establish a basis for future pay raises, promotion, or separation.

    3. ____

4. A once-a-year job evaluation on the management level is sufficient in most companies.

    4. ____

5. A performance rating is important to point out strengths and weaknesses to employees.

    5. ____

6. It is wrong for a supervisor to discuss one employee's rating with another employee.

    6. ____

7. Discussing specific goals that are to be met in a future given period is one step in an effective job-appraisal interview.

    7. ____

8. It is unnecessary and a poor practice for a supervisor to allow an employee to comment on obstacles that interfere with the employee's job performance.

    8. ____

9. A supervisor's appraisal of an employee's performance should be based on an accurate and detailed job description.

    9. ____

10. Poor job performance can be the result of placing an overqualified person in a job that requires little thought or creativity.

    10. ____

Part C: MULTIPLE CHOICE Choose the response that best completes each statement. Write the letter of the response in the space provided.

Answers

1. On an employee rating form, the factor "number of days absent" is an example of a(n)
   a. Subjective factor.
   b. Performance appraisal.
   c. Objective factor.
   d. Critical incident.

    1. ____

2. Which of the following statements concerning performance appraisals is not true?
   a. A formal process that should normally occur about twice a year.
   b. Designed to provide a firm foundation for future employment-related decisions.
   c. Employees like to know how well they are doing.
   d. A systematic method for appraising the worth of a particular job.

    2. ____

3. Frank described his new performance-appraisal program to his employees as a forced-choice format. This means:
   a. He will be ranking employees against each other.
   b. He will be using pairs of descriptive statements for each factor to be rated.
   c. The format is being imposed on him by upper management.
   d. Employees will be required to select an evaluation system.

    3. ____

4. Becky wants to make sure that her ratings are fair to each employee, and so she plans to rate all employees on a given factor before moving to the next factor. This is
   a. Illegal; you cannot make this kind of employee comparison.
   b. Ineffective; it is too cumbersome to accomplish her goal.
   c. A good idea that can help her reach her goal.
   d. Only possible if employees agree to her system.   4. ___
5. Each of the following statements is true of critical incidents except
   a. They represent the most important aspects of a job.
   b. They represent the quality—good or bad—of an employee's work.
   c. They should be placed in the employee's file.
   d. They are used by the supervisor during an appraisal interview to support his or her ratings.   5. ___
6. The "sandwich" technique for performance appraisal includes each of the following except
   a. Start the appraisal with a compliment.
   b. Discuss the work that must be improved.
   c. Conclude the appraisal by saying something good about the employee's work.
   d. Avoid criticizing the quality of the employee's work.   6. ___
7. A written record of a performance-appraisal interview is a good idea
   a. Always.
   b. Never.
   c. If your appraisal has been negative.
   d. If you have developed rapport with the employee.   7. ___
8. Ann is meeting today with Elton to conduct a performance appraisal. During the appraisal interview she should
   a. Compare the accomplishment of Elton with other employees doing similar work.
   b. Agree on targets to be met in the period ahead.
   c. Provide an equal number of positive and negative comments about Elton's performance.
   d. Tell Elton that if he wants to keep his job, he is going to have to make her happy.   8. ___
9. A primary objective of a performance rating is to
   a. Help the employee to improve the quality of his or her performance.
   b. Comply with company policy.
   c. Make sure supervisors know what is going on.
   d. Allow employees to compare their performance with that of others.   9. ___
10. When Sal is finished appraising all his employees, he should
   a. Check to be sure he has about as many employees ranked low as he has ranked high.
   b. Prepare a comparable worth table.
   c. Compare his results with those of other supervisors to see how his work group stacks up.
   d. Follow through with employees and help them improve on their weaknesses. 10. ___

13 Counseling Troubled Employees

CHAPTER

LEARNING OBJECTIVES

After studying this chapter, you should be able to

1. Describe problem performance and distinguish between a neurotic person and a psychotic person.

2. Recognize the symptoms of a troubled employee.

3. Explain the general approaches to employee counseling, discuss its limitations, and know when a troubled employee should be referred to a professional counselor.

4. Identify the various kinds of absenteeism and know the recommended remedial approaches for each.

5. Recognize alcoholism and illegal substance abuse among employees and know the recommended remedial approaches for each.

CHAPTER STUDY GUIDE OUTLINES

Based on your study of the text chapter and/or your instructor's lesson presentation, complete the following outlines by supplying the correct answers for the numbered spaces. Some answers require more than one word to complete. Write the answers in the numbered answer column. Although you should rely principally on your recollection, you can use the textbook if you need help. Check your answers by referring to the keys at the back of this study guide.

▶ Problem Performers

CONCEPT   Problems with employee performance can often be attributed to troubling personal factors that arise from conditions not related to the job.

1. There are two types of problem performers.
   a. The employee who doesn't measure up to established standards of output or __(1)__. This is dealt with during performance appraisals.
   b. The employee whose behavior is distracting or disruptive to the normal conduct of operations. This is the subject of this chapter.

Answers

1. _____

2. Most people encounter brief periods in their lives when they have problems away from work that affect their __(2)__. This is often a __(3)__ condition and their work performance soon returns to normal.

3. Other people, susceptible to stress, have prolonged performance lapses.
   a. These people can be described as __(4)__.
   b. It's likely the problem is emotional rather than physical.
   c. These troubled people can be referred to as __(5)__.

4. Supervisors must deal both with employees whose problems are temporary and with those whose problems are chronic.
   a. Severely disturbed employees should be referred to the organization's __(6)__ program.
   b. Personal problems of employees become a concern of the supervisor when the performance of the troubled employee becomes unsatisfactory.
   c. Skilled supervisors who really care and take the time to practice their listening skills can provide invaluable aid to troubled employees.

5. One in five workers is subject to emotional upsets that visibly disturb work. They may demonstrate their emotional distress
   a. Through hostility, the aggressive expression of anger on the job.
   b. Through withdrawal. They retreat from social interaction and confrontation.

6. Examples of troubled employees include
   a. Psychotic employees—people who are seriously ill. Schizophrenia, or split personality, is an example of a psychosis. These problems are beyond the scope of supervisors.
   b. Neurotic employees (most of us are neurotic to some degree)—these people may have exaggerated fears, need to prove themselves, and are irritable, hostile, opinionated, timid, or aggressive.

7. Accident-prone employees—according to DuPont researchers—"are victims of their own bottled-up emotions, which they turn against themselves."
   a. The fact that a safety rule has been violated is more important than why it was violated.
   b. Emotionally disturbed employees should not be pampered in safety-related matters. It may increase their demands and aggravate their injuries and the danger to others.

2. _____

3. _____

4. _____

5. _____

6. _____

8. Many people suffer from work addiction and use work to retreat from reality.

   a. __(7)__ tend to be nonproductive and may cut down on the output of others.

   b. They are usually moral, ambitious, honest, and loyal.

   c. They need professional therapy aimed at improving self-understanding, flexibility, creativity, and a __(8)__ between home and work.

9. Supervisors cannot ignore their troubled employees.

   a. In addition to dealing with them for the sake of sociological and humanitarian reasons, these employees are __(9)__ to have on the payroll.

   b. Most problems created are __(10)__ unless unattended by the supervisor.

   c. Supervisors should be concerned about

     (1) __(11)__ problem employees in the first place.

     (2) Handling them on the job so they can reach an __(12)__ level of performance with the least overall disruption to the company's performance.

     (3) Recognizing problems that are so serious they need __(13)__ attention.

7. _____

8. _____

9. _____

10. _____

11. _____

12. _____

13. _____

2▶ *Troubled Employees*

CONCEPT   It is important that supervisors recognize the behavioral symptoms of troubled employees before the job performance of these workers is adversely affected.

1. Troubled employees' symptoms differ widely but reactions are surprisingly alike.

   a. They tend to __(14)__ from reality—they overuse sick leave, believe supervisors are against them, and blame others for their problems.

   b. Are perpetually __(15)__, given to baseless worries, tire easily, are suspicious, and so forth.

   c. Some drink heavily, abuse drugs, are __(16)__, or have ungovernable tempers.

2. Because even emotionally healthy people encounter __(17)__, supervisors need to be alert to the symptoms of stress and rely on their counseling skills to help employees work through their problems. The causes of stress include

14. _____

15. _____

16. _____

17. _____

a. Physical or human environment (noise, odors, discrimination, boredom).

b. __(18)__ factors (anxiety over job security).

18. _____

c. __(19)__ factors (interpersonal friction with co-workers).

19. _____

▶3 *Employee Counseling*

CONCEPT Counseling—within carefully prescribed limits—offered by a supervisor to a troubled employee may improve performance by providing a degree of relief from anxieties.

1. A supervisor's counseling efforts begin by creating an __(20)__ atmosphere.

20. _____

a. Reassure troubled employees that you are trying to help them keep or enjoy their jobs more.

b. Make it clear that you are not looking for ways to punish or __(21)__ them.

21. _____

2. Employee counseling is ultimately a __(22)__ problem-solving technique that deals with job-related conditions.

22. _____

a. The goal of the supervisor is to enable employees to __(23)__ and release the pressures that are adversely affecting performance.

23. _____

b. Supervisors are not psychologists or social workers, but should be expert at recognizing problems and providing emotional support for employees' efforts to solve their problems.

3. Supervisors build a strong foundation for the counseling they must provide if they believe

a. People can and must be __(24)__ for their own actions.

24. _____

b. Employees should __(25)__ their own problems.

25. _____

c. It is important for the solution to employees' __(26)__ problems to conform to their beliefs and values, not to the supervisor's.

d. Convey a profound concern for the importance of others' feelings.

26. _____

e. The troubled employee has an important need to release pent-up feelings, emotions, and stresses, which psychologists call __(27)__ .

27. _____

4. Ten rules to help supervisors provide the best counseling of employees:

a. Let the employee control the direction of the session.

b. Give undivided attention to the employee.

c. Listen __(28)__ to what the employee has to say.

28. _____

  d. Convey in every way, your attentiveness, receptivity,
     and empathy.
  e. Don't __(29)__, interrupt, criticize, or offer advice.   29. _____
  f. Look beyond what the employee says to determine
     if he or she is telling you something deeper than
     what appears on the surface.
  g. Use __(30)__ to encourage thc cmployee to provide   30. _____
     an expanded explanation of a brief remark.
  h. Don't express surprise or judgment at anything the
     employee says.
  i. Use __(31)__ questions to encourage the employee   31. _____
     to take the initiative on the next appropriate action.
  j. Develop skill at reflecting feelings—bouncing back
     to an employee the emotional essence of what he or
     she conveyed to you.

5. A counseling __(32)__ is aimed at helping employees   32. _____
   to unburden themselves.
  a. Never mix a counseling interview with some other
     action you need to take.
  b. Results will take time and patience.
  c. Results may include improved ability to handle
     future problems, and a more relaxed employee,
     capable of clarified thinking and redirected energy.
  d. Don't expect __(33)__ in return. If successful, employ-   33. _____
     ees will feel they have solved their own problems.

6. Counseling sessions should be __(34)__ and not in-   34. _____
   terrupted.
  a. The supervisor should only initiate discussion of
     performance problems.
  b. If the employee voluntarily brings the problem to
     you, you can help most by nonevaluative listening.
  c. Employees with serious emotional problems may
     require five to ten 15- to 30-minute conversations
     just to gain their confidence.
  d. Ideally, a counseling interview should last between
     three-quarters of an hour to an hour.

7. Levinson advises that the basic steps in assessing an
   employee's needs are to
  a. Recognize the emotional distress.
  b. Relieve acute distress by listening.
  c. Refer cases beyond your limits to __(35)__ help.   35. _____

8. Levinson advises that if after two listening sessions you
   are having difficulty establishing confidence, you
   should __(36)__ the case (in confidence) to a medical   36. _____
   professional.

9. Two types of industrial professionals help troubled employees.

    a. A __(37)__, a fully qualified physician, can diagnose what an individual's trouble is and prescribe the proper kind of treatment.

37. _____

    b. A counselor, or industrial __(38)__

38. _____

       (1) Is a specialist, trained to listen understandingly to employee problems.

       (2) Has an advantage over the supervisor in gaining confidence because the counselor doesn't have __(39)__ to discipline, promote, or fire the employee.

39. _____

4 ▶ Reducing Absenteeism

       CONCEPT   Certain forms of absenteeism can be materially reduced by employee counseling.

1. Taylor observed that 60 percent of the people who are absent, are absent due to serious or chronic illnesses; 20 percent are absent due to acute short-term __(40)__, 10 percent are absent due to minor illnesses and don't report to work according to their attitude about their job; and 10 percent are completely __(41)__ and feign illness to enjoy a day off.

40. _____

41. _____

    a. A supervisor can have an impact on the bottom 20 percent (voluntary absence) by

       (1) Firming up absenteeism __(42)__.

42. _____

       (2) Being consistent in applying __(43)__.

43. _____

       (3) Trying to get at the reasons for frequent absences.

    b. __(44)__ can be effective in luring absence-prone workers back to the job.

44. _____

2. Counseling can be helpful for some people who are frequently absent. It can help people who

    a. Have a problem—real or imagined—getting to work.

    b. Have off-job pressures that are so strong that they weaken the resolve to get to work.

    c. Are easily led or misled.

    d. Think their work is boring, disagreeable, or unattractive.

    e. Have work relationships that are __(45)__.

45. _____

    f. Have off-job problems that need __(46)__ attention.

46. _____

    g. Have developed a habit of being absent or late.

3. Counseling will be difficult for other people who are __(47)__ absent. It will generally not be productive for people

47. _____

  a. For whom the work or the pay holds no strong attraction.

  b. Whose off-job pleasures have greater appeal than work.

  c. Whose willful absences are intended to disrupt or inconvenience the organization.

5 ▸ *The Problems of Substance Abuse*

CONCEPT Increasingly, supervisors must deal with problem performance that stems from substance abuse.

1. Counseling approaches for alcohol and drug abuse are similar despite the fact that there can be significant __(48)__ differences.

48. _____

  a. From a supervisory perspective, employees with __(49)__ problems are really just another type of problem employee.

49. _____

  b. Professional help is frequently needed for these employees.

  c. Early recognition of the problem by supervisors increases the chances for success.

2. Trice's study of the absence records of alcoholic employees found that

  a. Absences are spread __(50)__ the week.

50. _____

  b. __(51)__ absenteeism is frequent.

51. _____

  c. Tardiness is not a marked feature of the record.

3. Ten tips for counseling employees are

  a. Do not apologize for __(52)__ an employee.

52. _____

  b. Encourage an __(53)__ of the declining work performance.

53. _____

  c. Do not treat drinking as a moral issue—it is an illness.

  d. Do not suggest moderation—alcoholics cannot, initially, voluntarily control drinking habits.

  e. Do not be distracted by excuses.

  f. Do not accept the assertion that help has already been consulted.

  g. Remember that the __(54)__ should be given an opportunity for treatment and rehabilitation.

54. _____

  h. Emphasize that your major concern as a supervisor is the employee's poor work performance.

i. State that the decision to accept assistance is the employee's __(55)__.

j. Give the employee a chance to take treatment, but make it clear his or her job is on the line: __(56)__.

4. The supervisor's role in employee drug abuse is
   a. __(57)__.
   b. Prevention of use and sale on company property.
   c. Counseling—the same techniques as used for alcohol counseling.
   d. Referral.

5. In counseling employees with major illnesses, the supervisor should
   a. Allow the employee to decide whether, and how, to tell other employees.
   b. Develop a __(58)__ role for the employee.
   c. Avoid other special treatment and expect the employee to follow all rules, regulations, and standards of performance.

55. _____

56. _____

57. _____

58. _____

COMMENTARY ON SELF-APPRAISAL FROM THE TEXT

This exercise tests your knowledge and recall of a number of basic concepts and techniques regarding employee counseling. With few exceptions, the statements are clearly true (representing sound practice) or false (representing unsound practice).

Items 1, 2, 4, 5, and 6 stress a general understanding of counseling concepts.

Items 5, 12, and 13 highlight the recognition of employees who need counseling.

Items 7, 8, 10, 14, and 15 emphasize a knowledge of counseling techniques.

Items 3, 9, and 11 underscore the need to differentiate between the kinds of employees who can be counseled successfully by supervisors and the ones who should be referred to professional counselors as quickly as possible.

SELF-CHECK OF YOUR PROGRESS

Part A: COMPLETION An important term or phrase is needed to complete each of the following statements. Write the missing term in the space provided in the answer column.

1. A ____ is a mild emotional disorder in which employee feelings of anxiety, fear, or anger drive employees to unusual behavior that is often contrary to their own interests.

2. The process whereby healthy as well as disturbed individuals find a way to fit themselves to difficult situations by yielding, to a degree, and modifying their feelings and behavior is referred to as ____.

3. The release of accumulated feelings, emotions, and frustrations in a harmless fashion produces employee relief that is referred to as ____.

Answers

1. _____

2. _____

3. _____

4. ____ is a task-oriented problem-solving technique aimed at helping employees cope with some aspect of their work life.

5. ____ is a demonstration of antagonism on the part of a troubled employee, often caused by feelings of insecurity or inadequacy.

6. An employee suffering from ____ is affected by a severe mental disorder manifested by irrational or unmanageable behavior.

7. Some of the symptoms of ____ can appear in the form of headaches, ulcers, skin disorders, or coronary heart disease.

8. Partial absenteeism on the part of an employee could be a sign of ____ .

9. ____ is an especially serious difficulty, because an employee with this problem may try to involve others.

10. An employee who is in ____ avoids social contact, is very preoccupied, and keeps very much to him or herself.

4. _____

5. _____

6. _____

7. _____

8. _____

9. _____

10. _____

Part B: TRUE-FALSE   By writing T or F in the space provided, indicate whether each statement is true or false.

Answers

1. A workaholic is a dedicated, well-adjusted employee.

2. An employee who manages to visit the dispensary every day is probably exhibiting neurotic behavior.

3. A supervisor who threatens to lay off an employee because of the employee's emotional problems is really doing the worker a favor.

4. If counseling is effective, you can expect the employee to thank the supervisor for helping solve his or her problems.

5. A good counseling interview should be two to three hours long.

6. A supervisor who is making little headway with a troubled employee after two listening sessions should confidentially consult the company nurse or physician.

7. An accident-prone employee is probably just careless; there is very little chance that he or she is bothered by emotional or mental illness.

8. A trained professional counselor does not have the authority to discipline, promote, or fire the employee. Therefore, the employee is likely to place more trust in that person in a counseling session.

9. A good supervisor with troubled employees will provide more than just emotional support.

10. A supervisor needs to control the direction of an employee counseling session.

1. ____

2. ____

3. ____

4. ____

5. ____

6. ____

7. ____

8. ____

9. ____

10. ____

Part C: MULTIPLE CHOICE   Choose the response that best completes each statement. Write the letter of the response in the space provided.

Answers

1. Paul heard that one of his employees has been spending lots of money on lottery tickets. He should
   a. Refer the employee to a gamblers anonymous program.
   b. Do nothing until the employee's behavior affects productivity.
   c. Call the employee's spouse.
   d. Confront the employee about the problem.

1. ____

2. The causes of stress can be attributed to
   a. The human environment.
   b. Psychological factors.
   c. Psychosocial factors.
   d. All of the above.   2. ___
3. Allan regularly boasts of his drinking and sexual prowess. This is an example of a
   a. Schizophrenic employee.
   b. Psychotic employee.
   c. Neurotic employee.
   d. Workaholic.   3. ___
4. Each of the following statements about accident-prone employees is correct, except
   a. There are no accident-prone employees. Studies show accidents occur
      throughout the workforce.
   b. Studies show there are a group of employees who are involved in accidents
      more frequently than other employees.
   c. These employees tend to evade rules at work.
   d. These employees are victims of their own bottled-up emotions.   4. ___
5. Since problem employees tend to upset the morale of the work group, supervisors
   should be concerned about
   a. Hiring problem employees.
   b. Working with them to get an acceptable level of productivity.
   c. Determining when they need professional help.
   d. All of the above.   5. ___
6. Which of the following conditions suggests a worried worker?
   a. Reduced productivity.
   b. Sudden change in behavior.
   c. Difficulty in absorbing training.
   d. Each of the above is a sign of a worried worker.   6. ___
7. Seriously mentally disturbed employees should be treated by a fully qualified physician trained for the specialty. That person is called a
   a. Social worker.
   b. Psychologist.
   c. Psychiatrist.
   d. Family practitioner.   7. ___
8. Alexis often stays away from work in the hope of causing an inconvenience for her
   employer. She should be considered a(n)
   a. Chronic absentee.
   b. Aggressive absentee.
   c. Directionless absentee.
   d. Occasional absentee.   8. ___
9. An alcoholic employee
   a. Tends to be absent on Mondays and Fridays.
   b. Is frequently tardy.
   c. Has absences spread through the week.
   d. Tends to be absent about the same amount of time as other employees. 9. ___
10. When counseling alcoholic employees, you should
    a. Listen to them and develop plans to deal with the excuses.
    b. Encourage moderation.
    c. Apologize for having to discuss such a personal matter.
    d. Give the employee the opportunity for treatment and rehabilitation. 10. ___

CHAPTER 14 Building Cooperative Teams and Resolving Conflicts

LEARNING OBJECTIVES

After studying this chapter, you should be able to

1. Explain the formation, roles, and influence of informal groups in an organization.

2. Discuss the use of participatory management with groups of employees.

3. Explain the role of organizational development (OD) in helping to make teams more effective.

4. Identify the most common sources of conflict in an organization and describe some effective ways to solve conflict.

5. Discuss ways in which cooperation can be obtained from associates, staff people, individuals, and groups.

CHAPTER STUDY GUIDE OUTLINES

Based on your study of the text chapter and/or your instructor's lesson presentation, complete the following outlines by supplying the correct answers for the numbered spaces. Some answers require more than one word to complete. Write the answers in the numbered answer column. Although you should rely principally on your recollection, you can use the textbook if you need help. Check your answers by referring to the keys at the back of this study guide.

▶ Group Dynamics

CONCEPT   Supervisors need to understand group dynamics—the complex behavior of groups of employees and of employees within groups.

Answers

1. Jobs today involve more __(1)__ between individuals and departments, and they demand close cooperation among all parties.

   a. __(2)__ groups are set up to carry out work in the best way.

   b. __(3)__ groups are inevitable and can be very powerful.

   (1) Common skills, experiences, or even proximity may cause informal groups to form.

1. _____

2. _____

3. _____

(2) Membership in a group comes gradually; in return, the individual accepts and carries out the interests and behavior of the group.

   (a) Bonds of the group are __(4)__ when the group is formed for protection or support.

c. Informal leaders __(5)__ and guide group opinion.

d. A supervisor's relationships with informal groups are important.

   (1) Informal groups cannot be ignored.

   (2) They can be __(6)__.

   (3) They cannot be given too much attention at the expense of employees outside the group.

2. Group behavior has its own set of characteristics.

a. The personality of the group is stronger than that of any individual.

   (1) A group's personality reflects the outlook and work habits of the various individuals.

   (2) It will bring out the best or worst in some individuals and submerge the individual tendencies that are __(7)__ by the group.

b. Each group sets its own __(8)__ of conduct or norms.

   (1) Group norms may be in conflict with the company's or supervisor's methods of doing things.

   (2) The group will support group standards.

      (a) Individuals that do not conform are __(9)__ in some way from group activities.

3. Some groups are stronger—more cohesive than others. In cohesive groups

a. Members of cohesive groups are willing to make __(10)__ for the good of the group.

   (1) Are enthusiastic about what the group is doing.

   (2) Enjoy a common sense of identity and feel close to each other.

b. A cohesive group has a greater similarity of output among its members and higher productivity if the group's norm supports the organization's goals.

c. High cohesiveness also has its __(11)__. It may

   (1) Restrict __(12)__ by individuals.

   (2) Withhold unpopular views.

   (3) Fail to confront areas of __(13)__.

   (4) Suppress __(14)__ from individual members.

4. The most likely potential problems caused by groups are its ability to create mass resistance and its ability to pressure individuals to conform to group standards.

4. _____

5. _____

6. _____

7. _____

8. _____

9. _____

10. _____

11. _____

12. _____

13. _____

14. _____

5. Supervisors who are knowledgeable about group dynamics will treat each person as individually as possible without challenging the prerogative of the group the individual works in.

6. Work groups are good at __(15)__ .

   a. A group's ability to use jointly held know-how needs to be tapped by supervisors.

   b. Getting group involvement to solve problems is called "participation."

15. _____

▶2 *Group Participation*

CONCEPT   A participative approach tends to enhance a supervisor's effectiveness with employee groups.

1. You should permit groups to set their goals along with you and show them that these goals are obtained through teamwork. Make your role that of a __(16)__ .

   a. Make it clear you retain a __(17)__ over decisions.

   b. Establish ground rules for group participation.

   c. Provide enough information for the group to see situations as you do.

16. _____

17. _____

2. That the effectiveness of group participation—from suggestion systems to dramatic experiments with self-managing work teams—is based on the sharing of knowledge and information to gain cooperation (see text Figure 14-1). Each participation program recognizes

   a. Widespread desire of many employees to be more __(18)__ in their work organizations.

   b. That the predictable joint result of such participation is better quality decisions and employees __(19)__ to carrying them out successfully.

18. _____

19. _____

3. The supervisor can benefit from group participation if the group's perception is that the conclusion you wish is good for the __(20)__ . Remember

   a. Without group support your chance of achievement is slim.

   b. Your best chance for winning group support is to let the forces within the group itself work toward a decision with __(21)__ from you.

20. _____

21. _____

3 ▶ *Developing Cooperative Teams*

CONCEPT   Supervisors can apply the methods and skills of organizational development to improve the operation of their work teams.

1. __(22)__ is an approach to creating and sustaining high-involvement, high-performance organizations, and their subunits. It assumes

   a. Employees have much to offer, want to do so, and will grow and mature through various activities.

   b. That highly effective teams are essential to organizational success.

   c. That most organizations have been __(23)__, filled with conflict, and are too rigid to respond to their environment.

2. Organizational development consists of a series of steps including data collection, action-planned development, implementation of __(24)__, and evaluation of results.

3. Organizational development interventions include

   a. Process consultation—helping others see themselves and their behavior more clearly.

   b. Feedback mechanisms—collection of data and perceptions from others that are then provided to an individual or group.

   c. __(25)__ groups—unstructured small-group interactions.

   d. Job design and strategic approaches.

   e. __(26)__ is a popular intervention. It

   (1) Involves an activity that encourages members to explore how they work together.

   (2) Identifies the nature and intensity of their problems.

   (3) Develops more effective ways of interacting with each other.

   (4) Focuses on trust, taking risks, sharing significant information with each other, and providing support and encouragement to one another.

   (5) Involves the supervisor as both a part of the team and the __(27)__.

22. _____

23. _____

24. _____

25. _____

26. _____

27. _____

4 ▶ *Resolving Conflict*

CONCEPT   A limited amount of conflict within or between groups is to be expected; intense or disruptive conflict, however, should be resolved without delay.

1. Conflict is __(28)__ and in small amounts can be a good thing.

28. _____

2. The main sources of conflict include
   a. Different ideas about what should be done and how to do it.
   b. Departments that are at __(29)__ .

   29. _____
   c. The __(30)__: how it is laid out and supervised. The supervisor should be alert to

   30. _____
      (1) The appearance of an unfair allocation of tools, materials, supplies, and other resources.
      (2) Disagreements about what is important and what is not.
      (3) Changes at work that imply a change in status.
      (4) A sense of __(31)__ among employees.

      31. _____
      (5) A lack of stability in departmental operations.

3. __(32)__ is usually productive and differs from conflict, which is generally unproductive, pitting employees against each other in pursuit of their own goals.

   32. _____

4. A five-step approach to handling conflict is to
   a. Decide what it is that you wish to have accomplished.
   b. Call together the people who can best settle the issue.
   c. Be ready to __(33)__ , not hand out edicts.

   33. _____
   d. Not be distracted by the red herring of personalities.
   e. Focus attention on mutually beneficial __(34)__.

   34. _____

5. __(35)__ (TA) simplifies interactions that take place between people. It maintains that there are four views of relationships that can be held by employees and/or supervisors.

   35. _____
   a. I'm not okay. You're not okay.
      (1) This is a negative view—implies dissatisfaction with the employee's and the supervisor's behaviors.
      (2) This is like a child quarreling with a parent.

b. I'm not okay. You're okay.

   (1) Shows a loss of self-respect.

   (2) Places responsibility on the boss's shoulders—supervisors should get out of the role of __(36)__.

36. _____

c. I'm okay. You're not okay.

   (1) This is a __(37)__ role, treating employees like children.

37. _____

   (2) It invites rebellion or loss of hope that the employee can satisfy the supervisor.

d. I'm okay. You're okay.

   (1) This is a __(38)__ way to handle conflict.

38. _____

   (2) It is based on mutual respect.

   (3) Each person tries to understand, even if he or she does not agree with the other person's point of view.

   (4) It is called "__(39)__" (and can be effective if done honestly).

39. _____

5 ▶ Securing Cooperation

CONCEPT Cooperation from employees and associates can be encouraged by showing how cooperation protects or advances their interests.

1. People don't cooperate if they see no personal __(40)__ in doing so.

40. _____

2. To win cooperation, one must find out what people __(41)__ from work and satisfy those desires.

41. _____

3. Gaining cooperation from other supervisors requires __(42)__ sacrifice.

42. _____

a. Do not make your department look good at the __(43)__ of another department.

43. _____

b. Be willing to __(44)__.

44. _____

c. Avoid hairsplitting when allocating charges and responsibilities.

d. Let other supervisors run their own shows.

4. Since the success of staff people is dependent on gaining the cooperation of the supervisor, the axiom "__(45)__" is very true.

45. _____

5. Respect for others' points of view is the best way to avoid misunderstanding and gain willing cooperation.

6. Supervisors can be more effective if they create an atmosphere that encourages __(46)__.

46. _____

7. Sensitive supervisors have two advantages over less sensitive supervisors.

   a. They can avoid unnecessary human problems.

   b. They can blunt the edge of problems and conflicts because subordinates __(47)__ to try.

47. _____

COMMENTARY ON SELF-APPRAISAL FROM THE TEXT

This exercise covers the full range of key concepts in the chapter: group dynamics, participation, conflict resolution, and cooperation. The correct answers can generally be traced directly to statements in the text.

1. False. There is no way to prevent the emergence of informal groups within an organization.

2. True. Practices that stem from what a group believes to be right or wrong constitute a norm. The shelf-stockers apparently believe that washing up early is right; thus, this practice is a norm.

3. True. The specific reasons may vary, but informal groups are formed to satisfy any sort of special interests, all of which may not necessarily be related to work.

4. False. Supervisors who approach participation properly, as specified in the text, need not sacrifice their authority.

5. True. Sharing and participation are almost synonymous.

6. True. Legally restricted matters are among those items not generally considered suitable for participatory management, as shown in Figure 14-1 in the text.

7. False. OD programs recognize that employee needs are important and that too many organizations have highly structured work environments where those needs are not being met.

8. False. OD interventions include a number of steps but do not separate those steps from the actual intervention.

9. True. Supervisors not only learn to share some of their power with group members but find that when this occurs, in the eyes of their group members, they are more appreciated and respected.

10. False. Bickering and conflict become indicators of poor morale only when they begin to dominate organizational relationships. A certain amount of each is considered healthy and helps to relieve tension and clear the air.

11. True. Whenever there isn't enough of a valued material, tool, or facility to go around, it can be considered a scarce resource, over which conflicts may arise.

12. True. Bargaining and compromise may not yield the best solutions, but they are common ways to resolve conflicts. The best results are generally believed to come from a problem-solving approach.

13. False. Neither a parental nor a childish approach in TA will lead to better relationships. Only an adult (or mature) approach is considered to be effective.

14. False. As Herzberg pointed out, pay is not a satisfier for many people. Motivation to cooperate usually depends upon the satisfaction of psychological needs—social, esteem, self-fulfillment.

15. True. Sensitivity to interests and needs helps to lead a supervisor to ways of showing others how their cooperation will yield satisfaction.

SELF-CHECK OF YOUR PROGRESS

Part A: COMPLETION   An important term or phrase is needed to complete each of the following statements. Write the missing term in the space provided in the answer column.

Answers

1. ____ uses a variety of intervention methods, like team building, to create more effective organizations and their subunits.

2. Spontaneous groups of employees who have common personal interests or who work toward common job goals, whether or not these goals are set down by management, are called ____.

3. A ____ is a team of employees assigned by management to work together in a prescribed way toward goals established by management.

4. The beliefs held by a group about what is right or wrong concerning work performance are referred to as ____, or standards of conduct.

5. A relatively healthy struggle among individuals or groups within an organization to excel while striving to meet mutual goals is referred to as ____.

6. A salesperson keeping a pool car when unneeded just to keep another person from using it is an example of unhealthy ____.

7. One method of improving relationships between people is based on an understanding of each individual's parental, childish, or adult attitudes towards one another. It is referred to as ____.

8. ____ is a measure of voluntary cooperation and the intensity of desire to meet common work goals.

9. Using the language of transactional analysis, when a supervisor is responding to an employee using a parental role, it is like saying, "I'm okay. You're ____."

10. Another word for the transactional analysis concept of "I'm okay, you're okay" is ____.

1. _____

2. _____

3. _____

4. _____

5. _____

6. _____

7. _____

8. _____

9. _____

10. _____

Part B: TRUE-FALSE   By writing T or F in the space provided, indicate whether each statement is true or false.

Answers

1. An important first step in dealing with conflict in your department is to decide what it is you want to have accomplished.

1. ____

2. Often people don't cooperate because they see no personal advantage in doing so.

2. ____

3. One of the key features of organizational development is to avoid collection and sharing of data with individuals and groups.

        3. ___

4. If a supervisor is really good at his or her job, no informal groups will form within the department.

        4. ___

5. Clarke is a very slow worker when he works by himself. His work pace could be expected to speed up if he were to become a member of a work group with a strong norm supporting fast work.

        5. ___

6. The supervisor should always expect an individual who is a good worker to resist the influence of group pressure.

        6. ___

7. Constant quarreling and continual confrontations among employees probably are a sign that something is lacking in the quality of supervision.

        7. ___

8. Most of the causes of conflict in a department are closely related to the work itself.

        8. ___

9. Since personality differences are the major cause of on-the-job conflict, the wise supervisor stresses these when resolving conflicts.

        9. ___

10. As a general rule, work groups are relatively poor at solving work problems because they are too concerned with the personalities involved.

        10. ___

Part C: MULTIPLE CHOICE Choose the response that best completes each statement. Write the letter of the response in the space provided.

Answers

1. Deborah is a new supervisor seeking guidance on dealing with the formal organization of the company and with the informal work groups in the department. The best advice for her is to
   a. Forget the informal groups; there is nothing she can do about them anyway.
   b. Give formal groups first priority, but give some conscious attention to working with informal groups.
   c. Concentrate on dealing with the informal groups; that's where the real influence is.
   d. Try to become a trusted and equal member of all the informal work groups in the department.

        1. ___

2. In responding to informal groups, the supervisor should
   a. Accept the fact that the existence of informal groups is inevitable and that the groups will have considerable influence.
   b. Make every effort to keep these groups from forming.
   c. Realize that informal groups have little practical effect and therefore don't call for much attention.
   d. Recognize that the existence of informal groups is an important danger sign that supervision is inadequate.

        2. ___

3. Tom has made it clear to his employees that he demands their complete loyalty and that workers had better not look to informal relationships for any support on the job. This approach is
   a. The standard one in large organizations today.
   b. The best policy because it makes it clear who is the boss.
   c. Not likely to succeed, because employees have some legitimate loyalty to their informal groups
   d. Likely to weaken the informal groups even if it does not eliminate them.

        3. ___

4. The management technique of participation relies primarily on the work group's ability to
   a. Give instructions to employees.
   b. Solve operating problems.
   c. Decide on who should be hired and fired in the department.
   d. Take disciplinary action against employees who do poor work.   4. ___

5. Clara believes that the goals of informal work groups are always opposed to the best interests of the organization. This belief is
   a. True of strong groups but usually not true of weak groups.
   b. Correct.
   c. Usually true of groups that have a single influential leader.
   d. Mistaken.   5. ___

6. A person who has lost self-respect or places all of the responsibility on the boss's shoulders, in the terms of transactional analysis, is saying
   a. "I'm not okay. You're not okay."
   b. "I'm not okay. You're okay."
   c. "I'm okay. You're not okay."
   d. "I'm okay. You're okay."   6. ___

7. Allen finds that there is a moderate amount of competition among the employees in the department he has been assigned to supervise. The competition probably is
   a. Productive.
   b. Destructive.
   c. The result of resources being too limited.
   d. Correctable if personality conflicts can be eliminated.   7. ___

8. Harriet has been bothered by a continuing conflict between two repair workers in her department over responsibility for keeping the parts bins stocked. Her first step in resolving the conflict should be to
   a. Explain the company procedure for stock maintenance.
   b. Decide on what she wants to accomplish.
   c. Call the employees in question to the office for a meeting.
   d. Tell the employees they had better stop arguing or they will both face disciplinary action.   8. ___

9. Employees who are in conflict are more willing to compromise when the supervisor
   a. Gives definite instructions on how they will settle the conflict.
   b. Makes it clear that no bickering or negotiating will be allowed.
   c. Is able to find a course of action that will benefit both employees.
   d. Refuses to get involved in what is essentially a private matter between the employees.   9. ___

10. The success of staff people in a company depends on
    a. The cooperation of supervisors and other managers.
    b. Portraying supervisors in a bad light.
    c. Successfully imposing their views on managers who don't want to accept them.
    d. Avoiding disagreements or differences of opinion with supervisors and other managers.   10. ___

CHAPTER

15 Keeping People, Plans, and Programs on Track

LEARNING OBJECTIVES

After studying this chapter, you should be able to

1. Understand the dual nature—judgmental as well as problem solving and decision making—of the supervisor's role in carrying out the control function.

2. Define and recognize a control standard, and explain and evaluate the sources of these standards.

3. Discuss the four steps in the control process and explain the three major types of controls.

4. Identify the six major areas of organizational control that guide supervisory actions and explain the technique of management by exception.

5. Discuss employee resistance to controls, explain some of the ways to reduce it, and explain the relationship of management by objectives to the control process.

CHAPTER STUDY GUIDE OUTLINES

Based on your study of the text chapter and/or your instructor's lesson presentation, complete the following outlines by supplying the correct answers for the numbered spaces. Some answers require more than one word to complete. Write the answers in the numbered answer column. Although you should rely principally on your recollection, you can use the textbook if you need help. Check your answers by referring to the keys at the back of this study guide.

▶ A Dual Role

CONCEPT   Supervisors act both as judges and problem solvers in an organization's control process.

Answers

1. The basic purposes of a supervisor's control function are to keep things in line and help meet __(1)__ and quality standards.

1. _____

2. Most supervisors are an integral part of the control system.

   a. In their __(2)__ role they observe what happens and compare that with what was supposed to happen.

2. _____

   b. In their __(3)__ role they must correct below-standard conditions and bring results up to expectations.

3. _____

3. __(4)__ are directly related to planning goals.

4. _____

2 ► Control Standards

CONCEPT   Effective controls are based on sound standards.

1. Control standards are specific performance goals that a product, service, __(5)__, individual, or __(6)__ unit is expected to meet.
   a. They are usually expressed __(7)__.
   b. Permissible deviation from __(8)__ is called tolerance.
2. Standards may be set by line and staff departments as well as supervisors.
3. Standards may be based on past performance, high hopes, or __(9)__: the best method of setting standards.

5. _____
6. _____
7. _____
8. _____

9. _____

3 ► The Control Process

CONCEPT   The control process involves standard setting, measurement, comparison, and corrective action.

1. The control process has four sequential steps. (See text Figure 15-1.)
   a. Set __(10)__ of quantity, quality, and time.
      (1) What is expected?
      (2) How much deviation can be tolerated?
   b. Collect data to __(11)__ performance.
      (1) Written data like time cards, production tallies, inspection reports, sales tickets.
      (2) Observation of employees working.
   c. Compare results with standards.
   d. Take __(12)__ action.
      (1) Find cause of __(13)__ from standard.
      (2) Take action to remove or minimize the cause.
2. Controls are most effective when applied at __(14)__.
   a. Preventive controls occur before the conversion process.
   b. __(15)__ controls occur during the conversion process.
   c. Corrective controls occur after the process is complete.
3. Many operating processes depend on __(16)__ or computer-driven control systems.
   a. Impersonal measurements can count, time, and record employee performance.
   b. Automatic controls arouse __(17)__ from many people.

10. _____

11. _____

12. _____
13. _____

14. _____

15. _____

16. _____

17. _____

4 ▶ Control Targets

CONCEPT   The primary targets of supervisory control are output, quality, time, materials, costs, and employee performance.

1. Types of controls.
   a. __(18)__ controls relate to standards of production.   18. _____
   b. Quality controls relate to quality standards.
      (1) Routine product or service __(19)__ should be   19. _____
          made.
      (2) __(20)__ predicts quality deviations.   20. _____
   c. __(21)__ controls relate to deadlines and time con-   21. _____
      straints.
   d. __(22)__ controls relate to inventory and material-   22. _____
      yield controls.
   e. Equipment controls are built into the machinery,
      imposed on the operator to protect the equipment
      or the process.
   f. __(23)__ controls help ensure that, for example,   23. _____
      staffing and scheduling meet cost standards.
   g. Employee performance controls
      (1) Are often inseparable from other controls.
      (2) Focus on actions and behaviors of individuals
          and groups of employees; for example, absences,
          tardiness, accidents, quality and quantity of work.
2. Budgets incorporate many controls and control standards.
   a. Are cost- or expense-related.
   b. Identify quantity of materials used and units to be
      produced.
3. __(24)__ permits the supervisor to let things run as long   24. _____
   as they fall within prescribed control limits.
   a. This helps minimize time spent by supervisors on
      controls.
   b. When things get out of line, the supervisor takes
      __(25)__ . (See text Figure 15-2.)   25. _____

5 ▶ Handling Employee Resistance

CONCEPT   A supervisor's handling of employee resistance to controls is a critical factor in the entire control process.

1. Supervisors must find ways to ensure that employees
   meet job standards, especially attendance, speed and
   care in feeding and servicing automatic operations, and
   relationships with other departments and with customers and client organizations.

Chapter 15   **123**

2. Supervisors must determine which employees can work with little control and which ones cannot.

3. Resistance to controls can be minimized by the following:
   a. Emphasize the value of controls.
   b. Avoid arbitrary or punitive standards.
   c. Be specific; use __(26)__ that set specific targets.
   d. Aim for __(27)__ rather than punishment.
   e. Make the penalty for nonconformance absolutely clear.
   f. Avoid __(28)__ that can't or won't be backed up.
   g. Be consistent in the application of controls.

4. Encourage employee __(29)__.
   a. McGregor maintained that many people need only job standards and they will provide their own controls.
   b. Some people need or expect controls from supervisors.
   c. Give employees the benefit of the doubt.

5. Management by objectives (MBO) is a planning and control process that provides __(30)__ with a set of goals or standards to be attained at each organizational control point.
   a. The objective-setting process is done annually.
   b. MBO goals are similar to performance goals.
   c. The assumption is that if all supervisors meet their goals, the organization will also meet its goals.
   d. MBO is the formalization of the principle of __(31)__.

26. _____

27. _____

28. _____

29. _____

30. _____

31. _____

COMMENTARY ON SELF-APPRAISAL FROM THE TEXT

The intention here is to provide you with an experiential opportunity to try out your comprehension of what represents good—and not so good—control practice for a supervisor. The text oversimplified differentiation by providing only good, bad, and doubtful ratings. You may see many gray areas and be able to defend choices that do not agree with the experts' scoring. Here, however, is the rationale behind the marking of each item.

1. Good practice. The standard is clear and quantitative.

2. Bad practice. The quality standard is vague and nonquantitative, and it is impossible to measure performance against it.

3. Bad or doubtful practice. The safety standard is bad for the same reason as given in explanation 2.

4. Good practice. Steve has placed a standard in a key, make-or-break, point.

5. Bad or doubtful practice. Steve is overcontrolling by imposing what appears to be far too many controls at that point, whether or not it is a critical one.

6. Good practice. Steve is relieving himself of some responsibility by practicing management by exception.

7. Bad practice. This standard appears to be based on "high hopes," rather than on historical or systematic analysis.

8. Bad or doubtful practice. If the majority of controls are corrective ones, then Steve is missing the opportunity to impose preventive and concurrent controls, which both save the expense of discard or rework of poorly completed work.

9. Bad practice. Not only is Steve overcontrolling, but he is unrealistic about employee resistance to control. He is trying to overpower resistance, rather than to find a workable way to reduce it.

10. Bad practice. The chances of Steve's being able to carry out this threat are small. Even he indicates that he may have to "go to the top," where support for both his punitive attitude and his vague standard of "up to snuff" will probably not be found.

SELF-CHECK OF YOUR PROGRESS

Part A: COMPLETION   An important term or phrase is needed to complete each of the following statements. Write the missing term in the space provided in the answer column.

Answers

1. Comparing measurements of results with standards is part of the supervisor's role in ____ control.

1. _____

2. When control measures show that one or more goals are being missed, the supervisor must engage in ____ to bring results back in line.

2. _____

3. ____ is the process of monitoring operations and taking action when needed to ensure progress toward desired goals.

3. _____

4. Effective control depends on ____ that define, as precisely as possible, the results that should be obtained from operations.

4. _____

5. Most standards cannot be exactly met every time; for this reason, standards usually allow a little leeway, called ____, that makes effective control practical.

5. _____

6. Of the four steps usually recognized in the control process, the last step is ____.

7. Product inspection is mainly intended to assist managers in ____.

8. Management by objectives has an important goal of increasing ____.

9. ____ controls take place before the conversion process begins.

10. Computer monitoring of employee performance is an example of ____ controls.

6. _____

7. _____

8. _____

9. _____

10. _____

Part B: TRUE-FALSE   By writing T or F in the space provided, indicate whether each statement is true or false.

Answers

1. Effective supervisory control consists simply of keeping employees in line and enforcing rules.

2. Typically, when a supervisor discovers some phase of operations that is not meeting standards, all the supervisor has to do is report the condition to his or her boss.

3. An operating unit—such as a billing department or a computer center—that provides a service rather than a physical product cannot truly be controlled because it is impossible to set standards.

4. The control standard for the thickness of output from a planing machine is 20 mm ± 0.5 mm. A board that is 21 mm thick exceeds the tolerance.

5. Basing control standards on past performance tends to cause problems in that standards become so high that they cannot be achieved.

6. If a control standard is to do its job, there must be some way of measuring performance that is relevant to the standard.

7. Marie runs the counseling department of a large university student services organization; she will probably be able to rely mainly on automatic control to keep the department running well.

8. Bruce is completely unwilling to delegate any decision-making authority in his casting department; this means that Bruce cannot use management by exception effectively.

9. Controls are established without regard to the goals set by the organization.

10. The steps in the control process must be followed in sequence.

1. ____

2. ____

3. ____

4. ____

5. ____

6. ____

7. ____

8. ____

9. ____

10. ____

Part C: MULTIPLE CHOICE   Choose the response that best completes each statement. Write the letter of the response in the space provided.

Answers

1. The most important purpose of the control process is to
   a. Keep employees under control.
   b. Reduce costs.
   c. Eliminate employee errors and carelessness.
   d. Guide the supervisor and the department to production goals and quality standards.

1. ____

2. If the supervisor's control responsibilities are divided into two roles, the second role chiefly involves
   a. Making measurements of operating results.
   b. Solving problems and making decisions.
   c. Making judgments about whether standards are being met.
   d. Observing inputs, processing, and outputs.   2. ____

3. When the standards for a department's results are set by engineers or planners outside the department
   a. The department supervisor has no control responsibility.
   b. The outside planners are responsible for seeing that the standards are achieved.
   c. The department supervisor usually still must set individual worker and work station standards to achieve the department standards.
   d. The outside standards should be viewed only as a loose guide that the supervisor is free to change.   3. ____

4. As a general rule, the individual standards a supervisor sets for employees should be
   a. Possible to attain with reasonable effort.
   b. Possible to attain with extraordinary effort.
   c. Impossible to attain, since this will increase motivation.
   d. Attainable by the very best workers but impossible for the average worker.   4. ____

5. Which of the following can be used to record data used to measure the results of operations?
   a. An employee time card.
   b. A sales ticket.
   c. A production tally.
   d. All of the above.   5. ____

6. Martha instructs her office manager to order a new supply of copying paper when there are still two boxes of paper on hand. She is using
   a. Preventive controls.
   b. Automatic controls.
   c. Concurrent controls.
   d. Corrective controls.   6. ____

7. The sales manager of a radio station gives each salesperson a travel allowance of $200 for the month. This is an example of
   a. Quality control.
   b. Time control.
   c. Cost control.
   d. Quantity control.   7. ____

8. Under management by exception, the supervisor
   a. Closely directs all employee actions at all times.
   b. Gives up the control function entirely to trusted employees.
   c. Makes no use of normal operating or product standards.
   d. Closely directs employee actions only when conditions go above or below control limits.   8. ____

9. The supervisor of a department with clear controls that are well understood by employees will
   a. Have to interfere less with the way employees do their jobs.
   b. Never need to give precise direction to employees.
   c. Have no need for the use of disciplinary action.
   d. Have no need to provide employees with direct feedback on their performance.   9.

10. Of the following, the key term associated with management by objectives is
     a. Exceptions.
     b Instructions.
     c. Self-control.
     d. Competition.

10. ____

CHAPTER 16 Controlling Costs and Budgets

LEARNING OBJECTIVES

After studying this chapter, you should be able to

1. Discuss the importance of recordkeeping and differentiate among unit costs, standard costs, and budgeted costs.

2. Explain the purpose of budgets in cost control, describe the cost variance report, calculate unit costs, and explain the way in which flexible budgets are designed.

3. Understand how to select cost targets, assign priorities to them, and recognize a belt-tightening program.

4. Identify and evaluate the principal sources of cost improvement ideas, list some positive approaches, and explain why some cost improvement suggestions might be rejected.

5. Discuss the reasons for employee resistance to cost reduction programs and describe several ways for securing workers' support and cooperation.

CHAPTER STUDY GUIDE OUTLINES

Based on your study of the text chapter and/or your instructor's lesson presentation, complete the following outlines by supplying the correct answers for the numbered spaces. Some answers require more than one word to complete. Write the answers in the numbered answer column. Although you should rely principally on your recollection, you can use the textbook if you need help. Check your answers by referring to the keys at the back of this study guide.

▶ Accounting Records

CONCEPT   Effective cost control begins with accurate records of costs as they occur and an understanding of the accounting reports that document them.

Answers

1. Supervisors have responsibilities for __(1)__ and also cost reduction.

   a. Accurate and __(2)__ records are essential for effective cost control.

1. _____

2. _____

b. Three basic measures of cost that supervisors should be familiar with are
   (1) __(3)__ costs—costs accumulated per unit of product or service processed or produced.
   (2) __(4)__ costs—unit costs set down as allowable costs against which the supervisor's cost performance is judged.
   (3) __(5)__ costs—cost guidelines issued to supervisors at the beginning of an accounting period.

3. _____

4. _____

5. _____

2 ▶ Budgeted Costs

CONCEPT   Budgets establish departmental cost standards and targets and are used to monitor cost performance.

1. Budgetary controls list __(6)__ expenses based on the expectation of a certain level of __(7)__.
   a. Allowable expenses become cost standards for the reporting period.
   b. The __(8)__ report issued by the accounting department tells departments if they met, exceeded, or failed to meet their cost standards. (See text Table 16-1)
      (1) Reports help identify areas where cost control efforts will have to increase and indicate areas where cost standards can be reduced.
2. Flexible budgets offer allowances for variations in justifiable expenses for varying levels of output. (See text Table 16-2)
   a. Flexibility is not necessarily proportional to changes in output.
   b. Some expenses, like rent, heat, light, and indirect labor, are __(9)__ costs that tend to remain the same regardless of output level.

6. _____
7. _____

8. _____

9. _____

3 ▶ Cost Improvement Strategies

CONCEPT   Cost reduction strategies can be either broadly focused or specific in nature, but their success depends on carefully planned priorities.

1. __(10)__ plans can be organization-wide or confined to the operations of a single department.
2. The most promising cost targets are
   a. Product or service costs.
   b. Process, or operations, costs.

10. _____

   c. Direct and indirect people costs. (Indirect costs support the __(11)__ of a line department, such as maintenance, material handling, inspection, housekeeping, and other service functions.)

11. _____

   d. Equipment and tool costs.

   e. Materials costs.

   f. Utilities costs.

   g. Communications costs.

   h. Information costs.

3. Short-term cost-target priorities are usually assigned to __(12)__ projects.

12. _____

4. Longer-term cost-target priorities are assessed to measure projects based on their __(13)__. Cost targets to address are selected according to ratings like

13. _____

   a. __(14)__: this choice may not identify the true cause of the high costs.

14. _____

   b. Easiest: a good way to start a cost reduction campaign.

   c. __(15)__: what problem needs attention first?

15. _____

   d. Fastest __(16)__: what project will give the fastest return on an investment?

16. _____

5. "Belt-tightening" programs are negative in nature, focusing not on cost "improvements," but rather on ways to

   a. Stop spending.

   b. Do without.

   c. Postpone what you can.

▶ 4 Cost Improvement Sources

    CONCEPT   Cost improvement ideas may be gathered from a variety of sources, using a number of proven techniques.

1. There are four good sources of cost-cutting ideas:

   a. Yourself: keep track of your ideas even if there is no current use for them.

   b. Your __(17)__: they know the job well, and if properly encouraged, will share good ideas.

17. _____

   c. Staff departments: industrial engineers and methods and systems people can provide expert help once you've pinpointed the cost targets.

   d. __(18)__: they can generate impressive results.

18. _____

2. Cost improvement techniques, often in combination, accentuate the positive ways to improve costs.
   a. Reduce __(19)__ .
   b. Save time.
   c. Increase output.
   d. Spend __(20)__ .
   e. Use __(21)__ more intelligently.
   f. Watch your inventories.

19. _____

20. _____
21. _____

3. Why are some money-saving ideas turned down?
   a. The idea doesn't pay off __(22)__ enough.
   b. Ideas are often in __(23)__ with one another.

22. _____
23. _____

5 ▶ *Employee Reactions*

CONCEPT Employee resistance to cost-cutting changes is likely to be high, so employees require special motivational efforts on the part of their supervisors.

1. Employees often feel cost cutting affects their __(24)__ .

24. _____

   a. They think most money is wasted through poor planning and misjudgment by all __(25)__ .

25. _____

   b. They need to be communicated with and shown that cost cutting helps them.

2. Union attitudes will be similar to, but often more contentious than, those of the rank and filc. Some cost reduction activities may be perceived as
   a. A __(26)__ strategy to scare employees.
   b. Strategies aimed at __(27)__ the union.

26. _____
27. _____

   c. Speed-up operations designed for more profit and fewer jobs.
   d. A misdirected effort since they are wrongfully addressed at workers when the real problem is poor management.
   e. A ploy in which management "cries wolf" about __(28)__ and then switches jobs overseas.

28. _____

3. The best ways to reduce resistance and build support for cost improvement are to
   a. Talk to employees about cost reduction in terms of their __(29)__ .

29. _____

   b. Bring the cost picture down to earth.
   c. Set specific __(30)__ .

30. _____

   d. Invite participation.

e. Explain why and how changes will be made.

f. Train for __(31)__.

g. Report cost progress.

31. _____

COMMENTARY ON SELF-APPRAISAL FROM THE TEXT

This is a straightforward review of the concepts and methods presented in the chapter.

1. True. This fundamental need for good records was stressed in the opening questions.

2. True. Total costs are useful, but they need further interpretation to determine the effect upon them of varying volumes of output. Unit costs reduce (or translate) total costs into comparable measures. Thus, comparisons between current and past costs are valid and can be tracked, or plotted, to determine trends.

3. True. Costs are under control when actual costs are equal to, or under, budget. Control has been lost when costs are above the budgeted allowances.

4. True. Flexible budgets anticipate that while some unit costs may remain the same, the total expenses allowed for a budget-line item should reflect possible changes in the level of output.

5. False. Supervisors are mainly concerned with short-range, piecemeal cost reduction plans, but must participate in long-term, large-scale programs as well.

6. False. Edicts to postpone or stop spending are characteristic of belt-tightening programs, but they are not necessarily a part of all cost reduction efforts, especially those emphasizing cost improvement.

7. False. Cost reduction committees and quality circles have some features in common (participation and pooling of idea resources), but they differ in breadth of participation and in administrative approaches. There is more direction and control from above with cost reduction committees.

8. True. Especially in cost improvement ideas requiring rearrangement of processes and new machinery, money must be spent before the savings in costs can be attained.

9. False. Employees, as well as labor unions, tend to fear and resist cost reduction programs. They differ mainly in their responses, with labor unions being more outwardly contentious.

10. True. Cost improvements, like productivity and quality improvement, benefit from employee involvement in planning and problem solving.

SELF-CHECK OF YOUR PROGRESS

Part A: COMPLETION   An important term or phrase is needed to complete each of the following statements. Write the missing term in the space provided in the answer column.

Answers

1. Budgeted, allowable expenses become the cost ____ to be met during a given period.

1. _____

2. A ____ compares the actual expenses incurred against allowable expenses.

2. _____

3. Costs that tend to be constant and unrelated to the costs of production are thought of as ____ costs.

3. _____

4. ____ costs vary in relation to how much work a department is doing.

4. _____

5. A ____ is a plan, or forecast, of expenses that are allowable in a department.

5. _____

6. A cost reduction strategy of "do without" is an example of ____.

6. _____

7. Some companies have established ____ committees to initiate and oversee cost improvement activities.

7. _____

8. The cost of producing a single product is called a(n) ____ cost.

8. _____

9. ____ costs are those that can be clearly identified as adding value to the goods produced or service rendered.

9. _____

10. ____ costs are variable costs that are important to the production of goods or the rendering of services but which clearly do not add value to them.

10. _____

Part B: TRUE-FALSE   By writing T or F in the space provided, indicate whether each statement is true or false.

Answers

1. Cost reduction is the first responsibility of a supervisor.

1. ____

2. Supervisors should develop an understanding of the accounting terms their company uses.

2. ____

3. Flexible budgets are proposed by supervisors who just don't have the skills to control costs.

3. ____

4. Cost reduction programs can be organization-wide or departmental.

4. ____

5. It's a good idea to jot down cost-cutting ideas that might work at some time in your department.

5. ____

6. You can reduce cost rates by increasing the amount of work put through your department.

6. ____

7. Top management will never turn down a cost reduction idea.

7. ____

8. Employees often think poor management is the cause of most cost-related problems.

8. ____

9. Cost reduction programs can't be developed with employee participation and get results.

9. ____

10. Employees should receive training in the techniques of problem solving and methods improvement.

10. ____

134   Chapter 16

Part C: MULTIPLE CHOICE Choose the response that best completes each statement. Write the letter of the response in the space provided.

1. Cost guidelines or targets issued to supervisors at the beginning of an accounting period are called
   a. Unit costs.
   b. Standard costs.
   c. Budgeted costs.
   d. Variable costs.

Answers

1. ___

2. Costs that a department accumulates for each product or service delivered are called
   a. Unit costs.
   b. Standard costs.
   c. Budgeted costs.
   d. Variable costs.

2. ___

3. If the cost of labor and materials drops from $10,000 to $5000 and the number of units produced drops from 2000 to 1000, the unit costs have
   a. Gone from $5 per unit to $2.50 per unit.
   b. Stayed the same.
   c. Gone down $5000.
   d. Can't be determined from the evidence presented here.

3. ___

4. Kathy has noticed that costs on the toy assembly line have increased by 40 percent since one new employee replaced a retiring employee. Increasing the training for that employee is an example of addressing a cost target because it is the
   a. Most obvious.
   b. Easiest.
   c. Worst first.
   d. Fastest payback.

4. ___

5. A negative approach to cutting costs is to
   a. Reduce waste.
   b. Increase output.
   c. Save time.
   d. Do without.

5. ___

6. One of the results of postponing spending by deferring maintenance costs is that
   a. Short-term costs go down.
   b. The company increases the risk of equipment breakdown.
   c. Future maintenance costs may be more expensive.
   d. All of the above.

6. ___

7. Felix just had a cost-saving idea turned down by top management. Which of the following is least likely to be the reason the idea was turned down?
   a. The idea doesn't pay off quickly enough.
   b. The idea is in competition with other ideas.
   c. Top management didn't understand the idea.
   d. The idea generated too small a savings.

7. ___

8. The group typically most openly resistant to cost reduction ideas is
   a. Supervisors.
   b. Unions.
   c. Employees.
   d. Top management.

8. ___

9. Cost reduction committees have been replaced in many companies by
   a. Training programs.
   b. Indirect costs.
   c. Quality circles.
   d. Variable costs.

   9. ___

10. Each of the following ways to encourage employees to help with cost reduction programs is effective, except
    a. Explain the need for the program.
    b. Ask employees to recommend cost targets.
    c. State that it is hoped that layoffs resulting from the program will be temporary.
    d. Report cost progress.

    10. ___

CHAPTER 17 How and When to Discipline

LEARNING OBJECTIVES

After studying this chapter, you should be able to

1. Explain the goals for performance management and role of employee discipline, and identify the most common types of offenses that require action.

2. Discuss the range of employee responses to disciplinary action and describe those employees most likely to warrant such action.

3. Contrast constructive criticism with negative discipline, explain progressive discipline, and know the four elements of the "hot-stove" rule.

4. Discuss the emphasis placed on behavior rather than personality, list the prescribed steps in the behavior modification approach, and know the limitations placed on supervisory authority in disciplinary matters.

5. Explain the two criteria for just cause, recognize the necessity of due process, and discuss the importance of keeping proper support records.

CHAPTER STUDY GUIDE OUTLINES

Based on your study of the text chapter and/or your instructor's lesson presentation, complete the following outlines by supplying the correct answers for the numbered spaces. Some answers require more than one word to complete. Write the answers in the numbered answer column. Although you should rely principally on your recollection, you can use the textbook if you need help. Check your answers by referring to the keys at the back of this study guide.

1▶ Purpose

CONCEPT   Properly administered performance management systems serve to guide future behavior in constructive directions, while developing self-control among employees.

Answers

1. The purpose of __(1)__ systems is to encourage employees to meet or exceed established standards of job performance and to behave sensibly and safely at work.

1. _____

2. Employees who do not measure up to performance standards are subject to __(2)__.
   a. The imposition of a penalty by management on an employee for breaking a rule.
   b. Not designed to be __(3)__ but to act as a form of training so they can clearly learn what acceptable performance and behavior are.
   c. The use of penalties represents the admission by management that they may share in the blame for failure.
   d. Discipline should never be used as a show of __(4)__.
3. The most common behaviors that generate discipline include poor performance, __(5)__, insubordination, carelessness, negligence, horseplay, fighting, dishonesty, falsification of company records, abusive or obscene language, intoxication, or __(6)__.

2. _____

3. _____

4. _____

5. _____

6. _____

2 ► *Employee Expectations*

CONCEPT Employees will accept discipline when it follows preestablished policy, seems fair and just, and when it is applied consistently and equally for all.

1. Supervisors __(7)__ the wrongdoer, hear the case, and __(8)__ the penalty.
   a. Many employees see this as unfair because the supervisor acts as a police officer, prosecutor, judge, and __(9)__.
   b. It is a great responsibility requiring impartiality, good judgment, and courage.
2. Three major factors affect positive employee attitudes towards a disciplinary system:
   a. Employees are more likely to support discipline when they participate in its __(10)__.
   b. Employees' support is almost assured when they can see reasonable __(11)__ for it.
   c. When employee groups __(12)__ their own justice system, they are more likely to support the process.
3. When an employee breaks rules, supervisors should find out why, try to remove the reasons, and then if necessary, discipline.
   a. People break rules for work and nonwork-related reasons.
   b. They are less inclined to break rules when the supervisor is a good leader.
   c. If an employee has a __(13)__ problem, don't pry but do offer a willing and uncritical ear.
4. Employees should be able to expect justice and __(14)__ in disciplinary actions.

7. _____
8. _____

9. _____

10. _____

11. _____
12. _____

13. _____

14. _____

3 ▸ *Administrative Guidelines*

CONCEPT Discipline is most effective when applied constructively, progressively, and in accord with the "hot-stove" rule.

1. __(15)__ discipline is handled through constructive criticism or discussion rather than punishment.

15. _____

2. __(16)__ discipline increases the penalties for repeated rule infractions or continued substandard performance. Frequently, the penalties progress from an oral warning to a written warning, to suspension or layoff, and finally to discharge (see text Figure 17–1).

16. _____

3. The "hot-stove" rule consists of four essential principles of good discipline (see text Figure 17–2).
   a. Principle of advance warning.
   b. Principle of __(17)__ of punishment.
   c. Principle of impartiality.
   d. Principle of __(18)__.

17. _____

18. _____

4 ▸ *Supervisory Approaches*

CONCEPT Supervisors must learn to administer discipline firmly, but sensitively, and within prescribed organizational policies.

1. Administration of discipline can be an unpleasant experience but __(19)__ must face up to it.

19. _____

   a. You cannot overlook poor performance or misconduct.
   b. Problems rarely __(20)__ themselves.

20. _____

   c. You must learn to listen, intent on understanding what the problem is, before you __(21)__.

21. _____

   d. Your objective is to prevent __(22)__ problems, not to diminish an individual's self-esteem.

22. _____

2. __(23)__ is a six-step procedure that works effectively in combination with constructive criticism, counseling skills, goal setting, and employee involvement.

23. _____

   a. State the performance or disciplinary problem.
   b. Ask the employee for his or her __(24)__ of the problem.

24. _____

   c. Ask the employee for a __(25)__ to the problem.

25. _____

   d. Agree on a __(26)__ to solve the problem.

26. _____

   e. Give the employee an oral or written __(27)__.

27. _____

   f. Set up a date for a review.

3. How far an individual supervisor can go with discipline will depend on company policy and labor contracts.

4. __(28)__, not feelings, should determine disciplinary action.

28. _____

5. Warnings can be very effective if they are not just idle threats.
   a. Use a warning as an opportunity for __(29)__ criticism.

   29. _____

   b. Keep a __(30)__ record of all warnings—this will serve as important evidence in any future grievance hearings.

   30. _____

6. Some employee actions, such as drinking, sleeping on the job, or falsifying time records, require immediate action by the supervisor.
   a. __(31)__ can remove the employee from the work site immediately and permit you (and others in the company) to decide later if you can make a discharge stick.

   31. _____

   b. The past __(32)__ of an employee may be taken into consideration when disciplining.

   32. _____

   c. If you must discharge an employee, do it in __(33)__, with a colleague as a witness, with documentation.

   33. _____

      (1) Avoid being __(34)__; be tactful and assertive.

   34. _____

      (2) Provide details of his or her residual rights to any employee __(35)__.

   35. _____

      (3) Respond to questions or promise to obtain answers.

      (4) Have a plan to communicate your action to the rest of your __(36)__.

   36. _____

▶ 5 *Legal Ramifications*

CONCEPT   Discipline must conform to various legal requirements and be supported by documentation for just cause.

1. Legal requirements to demonstrate __(37)__ for disciplinary action include

   37. _____

   a. Prior notification of the types of performance or behavior that can lead to disciplinary action.
      (1) Notification can be made orally or in writing.
      (2) Company rules, regulations, and standards cannot cover everything, so it is important that supervisors communicate standards of __(38)__ and conduct clearly.

   38. _____

   b. Prior notification of the __(39)__ for unacceptable performance or behavior.

   39. _____

      (1) It's best when notification of penalties are written and visibly __(40)__ in the workplace.

   40. _____

      (2) Supervisors should regularly state what the penalties are and when they would be __(41)__.

   41. _____

(3) If you have a progressive disciplinary policy, the steps should be communicated in advance to employees.

2. __(42)__ guarantees the employee a fair and just hearing to ensure that the organization's policies and procedures have been followed. Specific documentation that help support a supervisor's actions include

   a. Regularly kept records like time cards and quality-control reports.

   b. Written complaints from __(43)__ and so forth.

   c. Examples of __(44)__ or careless work.

   d. Written summaries of __(45)__ and/or disciplinary conferences.

42. _____

43. _____

44. _____

45. _____

COMMENTARY ON SELF-APPRAISAL FROM THE TEXT

The items chosen here reflect the principles of positive, progressive discipline, as exemplified by the behavior modification approach and the hot-stove rule.

1. Likely. Rita is using a positive approach by emphasizing that good performance is rewarded.

2. Likely. Here, Rita tries to specify what the standards of acceptable performance are and to show that they are not concerned with trivial matters.

3 Likely. This, too, is a positive approach, treating discipline as an opportunity for training employees in the correct procedures.

4. Likely. This demonstrates that the rules are fair and also implies that other clerks will support any disciplinary action that is taken in their regard.

5. Unlikely. To discriminate for any reason is to violate the principle of equal treatment for all offenders.

6 Unlikely. To express value judgments about Toby as a person is to put him on the defensive, rather than to encourage a constructive approach to improvement.

7. Unlikely. Rita violates the principle of immediacy here. She should have found time to reprimand soon after she noticed an infraction.

8. Likely. Under the behavior modification approach, an invitation to the employee to make suggestions for solving the problem is an essential part of the disciplinary process.

9. Likely. Under the behavior modification approach, as well as for legal reasons, written notations of warnings will carry weight far better than recollections of conversations.

10. Unlikely. It is poor practice to assume that one discussion will result in improvement. Rita should have scheduled a followup meeting to review progress toward a reduction in misrings.

SELF-CHECK OF YOUR PROGRESS

Part A: COMPLETION   An important term or phrase is needed to complete each of the following statements. Write the missing term in the space provided in the answer column.

Answers

1. ____ is a step-by-step procedure to follow in stimulating acceptable employee practices following an infraction.

2. The need for ____ occurs when work rules are consistently violated.

3. Employees expect supervisors to use discipline to assure justice and ____.

4. ____ discipline occurs when the penalties for substandard performance get increasingly harsh if the condition is repeated.

5. The first principle of the hot-stove rule of discipline is to provide the employee with ____ .

6. The fourth principle of the hot-stove rule of discipline suggests that supervisors administer it with ____ .

7. Disciplinary action should be based on ____ , not hearsay.

8. ____ is the employee's legal right to a fair hearing before an impartial party with appropriate representation.

9. The temporary removal of an employee from work without pay until management determines the proper penalty for a rule infraction is called a ____ .

10. A ____ is a written or oral reprimand worded to give formal notice to an employee that repetition of a particular form of unacceptable behavior will draw a penalty.

1. _____

2. _____

3. _____

4. _____

5. _____

6. _____

7. _____

8. _____

9. _____

10. _____

Part B: TRUE-FALSE   By writing T or F in the space provided, indicate whether each statement is true or false.

Answers

1. Self-discipline exercised by employees is always better than discipline imposed on them.

2. Supervisors should regard discipline as a form of training.

3. The need for a supervisor to impose a penalty is always the fault of the individual worker.

4. If a supervisor gives an employee little chance to show initiative on the job or to have a say in how the job is performed, the employee may present discipline problems.

5. When an employee breaks a rule, it is important for the supervisor to take disciplinary action immediately.

6. During a disciplinary hearing, records developed on an ongoing basis over time are more persuasive than those reconstructed from memory just prior to a hearing.

7. Progressive discipline follows a sequence of increasingly more severe penalties.

8. The degree to which a union can participate in disciplining an employee is spelled out in the union contract.

1. ___

2. ___

3. ___

4. ___

5. ___

6. ___

7. ___

8. ___

9. Supervisors should make it clear to employees what penalties will occur if discipline is necessary.

9. ____

10. Due process guarantees that discipline will be accepted by the employee.

10. ____

Part C: MULTIPLE CHOICE Choose the response that best completes each statement. Write the letter of the response in the space provided.

Answers

1. The purpose of discipline is to
   a. Increase employee morale.
   b. Encourage employees to meet established standards of job performance.
   c. Increase overall productivity.
   d. Eliminate the need to impose penalties.

1. ____

2. Employees resent discipline from supervisors because
   a. It interferes with their creativity.
   b. Any person is naturally suspicious of authority.
   c. The supervisor has to act as police officer, judge, and jury.
   d. Most supervisors find it hard to be impartial.

2. ____

3. To meet the legal standard for just cause of a disciplinary action, the supervisor will be required to demonstrate each of the following except
   a. Prior notification to employees of the types of performance that could lead to disciplinary action.
   b. Prior notification to employees of the penalties for unacceptable performance.
   c. A written policy outlining the "hot-stove" rule.
   d. All of the above.

3. ____

4. Each of the following is a step in the behavior modification process except
   a. An opportunity to appeal the disciplinary action.
   b. Asking the employee for his or her view of the problem.
   c. Asking the employee for a solution to the problem.
   d. Agreeing on a plan to solve the problem.

4. ____

5. Due process is
   a. The right of any employee to be represented at a fair hearing.
   b. Temporary removal of a worker by management.
   c. The imposition of a penalty on an employee by management.
   d. Progressive discipline.

5. ____

6. Progressive discipline is
   a. The hot-stove rule of discipline.
   b. A punishment imposed to enforce discipline.
   c. Punishment that gets increasingly harsh with successive infractions.
   d. The result of failing to address the problem when it happened.

6. ____

7. Which of the following actions is not appropriate when a supervisor is investigating a possible infraction requiring disciplinary action?
   a. Check with witnesses.
   b. Look in company records.
   c. Refuse to listen to the employee's story.
   d. Speak to the boss or human resources manager.

7. ____

8. A principle that employees are entitled to a fair and just hearing with appropriate representation and the presentation of available evidence is referred to as
   a. Due process.
   b. Performance management.
   c. Behavior modification.
   d. Just cause.

8. ____

9. An attempt to redirect an employee's behavior into productive channels by pointing out mistakes, coaching the correct way, and encouraging the employee to do better is an example of
   a. Discipline.
   b. Constructive criticism.
   c. Due process.
   d. Just cause.   9. ___
10. When rules are broken at work, most employees hope
   a. That the person will get away with it.
   b. That the person will receive just and equitable treatment.
   c. That if the person is someone they like, he or she will receive special treatment.
   d. If the person is someone they don't like, he or she will be treated severely.   10. ___

18 Stimulating Productivity and Innovation

LEARNING OBJECTIVES

After studying this chapter, you should be able to

1. Calculate productivity ratios and percentages, and understand the relationships of outputs and inputs to rising or falling productivity rates.

2. Recognize the differing potentials of human factors and technological factors for productivity improvement.

3. Describe the principle of work measurement and the principle of, and procedure for, work sampling.

4. Understand and describe various approaches to methods improvement, including motion economy and value analysis.

5. Explain various approaches to creative thinking and innovation, including free association of ideas and brainstorming.

CHAPTER STUDY GUIDE OUTLINES

Based on your study of the text chapter and/or your instructor's lesson presentation, complete the following outlines by supplying the correct answers for the numbered spaces. Some answers require more than one word to complete. Write the answers in the numbered answer column. Although you should rely principally on your recollection, you can use the textbook if you need help. Check your answers by referring to the keys at the back of this study guide.

1 ▶ Understanding Productivity

CONCEPT   Productivity measures how much __(1)__ is being created by a given set of __(2)__.

1. Productivity measures how efficient a person or an operation is by comparing the value of the output with the cost of the input. It is frequently expressed by a rate or __(3)__:

$$\text{productivity} = \frac{\text{output}}{\text{input}}$$

Answers

1. _____

2. _____

3. _____

a. A productivity ratio can be established as a standard for a work activity.

b. It is helpful to compare current __(4)__ with this standard. This comparison is usually expressed as a percentage increase or decrease.

c. When productivity is discussed, it is usually discussed not in relation to the standard but whether the rate is increasing or decreasing.

2. In most organizations, your productivity performance will be judged on whether it is rising or falling.

a. If your output goes up while the size of the input remains the same, productivity will __(5)__.

b. If the size of your output goes down while the size of the input remains the same, productivity will __(6)__ (see text Figure 18–1).

3. Principles of productivity apply in all work settings.

a. The need for a reliable measure of output makes application difficult for some jobs.

b. Changes in quality requirements can raise or lower output without creating a real change in __(7)__.

c. Productivity measures should not focus only on labor costs but also the cost of power, equipment, and facilities, for example.

4. _____

5. _____

6. _____

7. _____

▶ 2 *Human Factors*

CONCEPT   Productivity can be made to increase by improving either technological or __(8)__ contributions, or both.

8. _____

1. Two factors can improve productivity (see text Figure 18–2).

a. Technological factors.

(1) Product or service design.

(2) Plant and equipment.

(3) __(9)__.

(4) Process layout and methods.

(5) Condition of material.

(6) Power usage.

(7) Information.

b. Human factors.

(1) Ability, __(10)__, motivation.

(2) Education, experience, level of aspiration.

9. _____

10. _____

      (3) Work schedules, training, organizational group-
          ings.

      (4) Personnel policies, leadership, __(11)__ practices.   **11.** _____

2. To minimize employee resistance to productivity
improvement

   a. Don't start up the __(12)__ at top speed.   **12.** _____

   b. Be prepared to show employees how, although the
need for manual skills may decrease, the change
may enhance their know-how and opportunities for
applying their mental skills.

   c. Expect that the greater the use of high-tech systems,
the greater the need for __(13)__ communications.   **13.** _____

   d. Take care not to allow the old, usually counterpro-
ductive, methods to creep back in.

   e. Don't try to sneak an improvement in on your
employees.

3. Job __(14)__ is the major unexploited factor to   **14.** _____
improve productivity.

   a. Productivity is improved when supervisors support
employees in their individual search for job satisfaction.

   b. There is a need to balance employee needs with the
organization's need for productivity and cost
control.

4. The __(15)__ movement focuses on the human element   **15.** _____
to improve productivity.

3▶ *Work Measurement*

      CONCEPT   Fundamental to productivity improvement is a knowledge of how
      much time it takes to get a particular job done.

1. __(16)__ is any method for finding how long it takes to   **16.** _____
do a job.

   a. Usually refers to how long it takes a person to perform a specific task.

   b. Can include machine assistance.

   c. May also measure physical effort and skill.

2. The main ways work is measured are
   a. __(17)__ studies—using some sort of stopwatch or historical records to measure production in a day, week, or month.
   b. Motion studies—measuring each motion required of a job.
      (1) Measuring units are called predetermined elemental time standards.
   c. Work __(18)__: making random observations of various activities. (See text Table 18-1.)
      (1) This is a good method for supervisors to use to get a quick idea of departmental productivity.
      (2) It measures what each employee is doing at the __(19)__ the employee is observed. Employees' activities are recorded under categories such as
         (a) Working.
         (b) Preparing to work.
         (c) Travel.
         (d) Delay.
         (e) Idle.
3. Work-measurement data are used to
   a. Estimate accurately how long future jobs will take.
   b. Establish __(20)__ work schedules.
   c. Provide work standards in terms of
      (1) Time allowed to get work done.
      (2) Number of output units to be produced in a time period.
   d. Estimate labor costs for a product or service.
   e. Provide a basis for __(21)__.
   f. Provide fundamental measures of productivity.

17. _____

18. _____

19. _____

20. _____

21. _____

▶ **4** *Methods Improvement*

CONCEPT   The systematic way for increasing productivity is to improve the methods used for performing work.

1. Methods improvement refers to changes in the way a task is performed to __(22)__, shorten time, or improve __(23)__ of a product or service.
   a. It is also known as work simplification, time-and-motion study, operations analysis, methods engineering, __(24)__, systems analysis, and so forth.

22. _____
23. _____

24. _____

b. It is often done by observing each segment of a job and then examining each segment for ways to do the job better.

c. Asking who, what, __(25)__, why, where, and how can lead you to find opportunities to improve productivity or cut costs.

25. _____

2. Five things can happen to a product or service during a work activity. One adds value; the other four may be __(26)__, are often costly, but do not add __(27)__.

a. The valued element: an operation that does something to improve or add value to the object.

26. _____
27. _____

b. The wasteful elements (even if they are necessary for some reason) include
   (1) Inspection.
   (2) __(28)__.
   (3) Delay.
   (4) __(29)__.

28. _____

29. _____

c. If you are attempting to improve your work methods, focus your attention first on the wasteful elements.

d. To analyze a job, look at it as if it were divided into three steps: __(30)__, do, and put-away. (See text Figure 18-3.)

30. _____

   (1) Makeready and put-away segments are prime candidates for elimination, combination, or for handling automatically.
   (2) The "do" operations are hard to eliminate, but they can lend themselves to speeding up, simplifying, or combining with another operation.

3. New and better methods can include __(31)__, combining, changing the sequence, and simplifying.

31. _____

4. Motion economy is the use of the human body to produce results with the least physical and mental effort. It is a way to help improve productivity.

a. Motions should be productive.

b. Motions should be __(32)__.

32. _____

c. Motions should be rhythmic.

d. Workers should be made __(33)__.

33. _____

e. Two or more tools should be combined into a single tool.

f. Tools and materials should be prepositioned.

g. Activity should be limited.

5. Automation and robotics decisions are usually made by engineering specialists and computer system experts.
   a. Office automation uses computerization to link together previously independent clerical and administrative activity.
      (1) Workflow automation programs these activities within the computer network itself.
      (2) The result of office automation has been a __(34)__ of office staffs and the work space allotted to those staffs.
   b. __(35)__ at the company-wide methods-improvement level focuses on the following questions:
      (1) Why are we doing this?
      (2) How can we do it better?
      (3) How can we achieve more with less?
   c. Whenever __(36)__ improvement takes place, supervisors should be alert to the following changes:
      (1) Accelerated time frames.
      (2) Less __(37)__ monitoring of output.
      (3) Closer coupling of an internal department's activities with forces outside the organization.
   d. An important role of the supervisor will be to __(38)__ employees about the relocations and displacements and to train them to handle the new systems.
6. The objective of value analysis is to retain only those __(39)__ functions the customers want—but at a lower cost; hence, it will focus on
   a. Simplifying a product's design features.
   b. Minimizing the amount and cost of materials used in it.

34. _____

35. _____

36. _____

37. _____

38. _____

39. _____

5 ▶ Innovation and Creativity

CONCEPT   Creative supervisors and employees are valuable sources of innovative ideas for improving work methods.

1. Supervisors play an important role in methods improvement because they
   a. Have the best, most practical ideas for small-scale work improvements.
   b. Have a better __(40)__ of the job than a worker.
   c. Must work cooperatively with methods engineers.
2. Creativity is the __(41)__ of ideas to solve problems that haven't been solved by following the same old routine.

40. _____

41. _____

a. A systematic method to generate innovative ideas
   is to
   (1) Narrow down the problem.
   (2) Learn to __(42)__.   42. _____
   (3) Persevere.
   (4) __(43)__.   43. _____
   (5) Build your confidence.
   (6) Use your unconscious mind.
   (7) Keep ideas __(44)__.   44. _____
   (8) Take __(45)__.   45. _____

b. Brainstorming is green-light thinking; when ideas
   emerge, don't stop to judge their merit.
   (1) After all ideas have emerged, start red-light
       thinking and evaluate their potential for im-
       proving methods.
   (2) Osborn's four rules for brainstorming are:
       (a) Don't __(46)__ ideas.   46. _____
       (b) Welcome ideas freely.
       (c) Strive for quantity.
       (d) Combine and improve.

COMMENTARY ON SELF-APPRAISAL FROM THE TEXT

This self-appraisal challenges you, not only to recall what you have read, but also to make interpretive judgments. As with most self-appraisals, the answers here can be debated. If you disagree, first try to understand the other point of view and then demand of yourself strong reasons for your position.

1. Ineffective. Measurement is the foundation stone of productivity improvement. Since the self-appraisal stated that the low productivity was "presumed," this should be verified by a productivity calculation to find where the department stands now.

2. Effective. A constant output and a declining input indicate rising productivity. No action need be taken: "Don't fix it if it doesn't need fixing." On the other hand, more improvement is usually welcomed, although the urgency is not apparent here.

3. Ineffective. Supervisors are more likely to be able to suggest improvements in the contributions of the human factor to productivity. Even if this were not true, the human factor should always be given attention, regardless of whether its potential for contribution is small.

4. Ineffective. Quality circles, as stated in the text, are directed at productivity improvement as well as at quality improvement. They deserve consideration, even if rejected for other reasons: not authorized, too time consuming, and so forth.

5. Effective. Work measurement is the foundation stone of methods improvement. Without the facts that it provides, the supervisor will be working in the dark.

6. Effective. Either department may be able to suggest ideas for reducing delays caused by shortages of materials.

7. Ineffective. Small improvements should be as welcome as large ones.

8. Effective. Under motion economy, the idea of making workers comfortable is recommended for productivity improvement.

9. Ineffective. Useful ideas are among the welter of ideas, useful or otherwise, obtained from the application of free association of ideas, either by individuals or by groups while brainstorming.

10. Effective. Brainstorming is most effective when it has a target to shoot at. It is a proven way to generate helpful solutions to problems, including those of productivity.

SELF-CHECK OF YOUR PROGRESS

Part A: COMPLETION   An important term or phrase is needed to complete each of the following statements. Write the missing term in the space provided in the answer column.

Answers

1. ____ compares the cost of the input against the value of the output.

1. _____

2. Ability, knowledge, and motivation are ____ factors to be considered in improving productivity.

2. _____

3. Supervisors who help their employees find job ____ can help increase productivity from the human side.

3. _____

4. ____ is any method of finding out how long it would take an individual to complete a certain task.

4. _____

5. ____ is a method of measuring how much of an employee's time on the job is spent productively on a job assignment.

5. _____

6. Using the human body most efficiently in accomplishing a particular task is ____.

6. _____

7. Methods improvement that is focused on a product rather than a process is ____.

7. _____

8. ____ is a top-down, broad-based approach to improvement that can lead to sweeping changes in goals and methods throughout an organization.

8. _____

9. ____ is another term for methods improvement.

9. _____

10. The expected time of an operation, based on past performance or work measurement, is the ____.

10. _____

Part B: TRUE-FALSE   By writing T or F in the space provided, indicate whether each statement is true or false.

Answers

1. Productivity measures are useful for industrial output only.

1. ____

2. Output may drop if quality requirements are raised.

2. ____

3. Quality circles have shown that involving concerned employees can improve productivity as well as quality.

3. ____

4. Work sampling serves as the fundamental measure of productivity.   4. ____
5. The best ideas for work improvement come from middle management.   5. ____
6. The greatest room for improvement in a job is in the value-added operations.   6. ____
7. The basis of methods improvement is work measurement or work-sampling data.   7. ____
8. Brainstorming is intended to generate a maximum number of ideas in a short period of time.   8. ____
9. Ergonomics is useful in designing more comfortable and productive work stations.   9. ____
10. Research has demonstrated that most good ideas are generated by a small number of very creative individuals.   10. ____

Part C: MULTIPLE CHOICE   Choose the response that best completes each statement. Write the letter of the response in the space provided.

Answers

1. Productivity is rising if
   a. Output remains the same and costs go up.
   b. Output goes down and costs remain the same.
   c. Output goes up and costs stay the same.
   d. None of the above.   1. ____
2. Technological factors that can improve production include
   a. Condition of materials.
   b. Individual education.
   c. Experience.
   d. Work schedules.   2. ____
3. Work measurement includes all of the following, except
   a. Finding out how long it takes to do a job.
   b. Surveys of employee job satisfaction.
   c. Amount of physical effort needed to do a job.
   d. Machine-paced work.   3. ____
4. All of the following are examples of work-measurement methods except
   a. Time studies.
   b. Time standards.
   c. Motion studies.
   d. Work sampling.   4. ____
5. Verene should consider using her work-measurement data to
   a. Establish reliable work schedules.
   b. Provide fundamental measures of productivity.
   c. Provide specific work standards.
   d. All of the above.   5. ____
6. Bill plans to conduct a work-sampling study of his department. Which of the following statements reflects an important element of a successful study?
   a. Regular observation over a reasonable time.
   b. Ignore any time spent preparing for work.
   c. Random pattern of observation.
   d. Don't let employees know the sampling is going to take place.   6. ____
7. Which of the following production steps of a job has the greatest room for improvement?
   a. Makeready.
   b. Do.
   c. Put-away.
   d. Don't.   7. ____

8. Value analysis focuses on reducing costs while maintaining the functions of
   a. Salary and fringe benefits.
   b. Technology and human factors.
   c. Use and esteem.
   d. Supervisors and employees.   8. ____
9. Ramesh has just heard that his company is instituting a company-wide reengineering of its operations. Which of the following changes is least likely to occur?
   a. Accelerated time frames.
   b. Less forgiving monitoring of output.
   c. Closer coupling of a department's activities with forces outside the organization.
   d. None of the above.   9. ____
10. Brainstorming rules include
   a. Discuss each idea fully before moving to the next idea.
   b. Strive for quality.
   c. Strive for quantity.
   d. Keep ideas focused on the target.   10. ____

CHAPTER ▶ **19** Raising the Quality of Products and Services

LEARNING OBJECTIVES

After studying this chapter, you should be able to

1. Explain the meaning of quality, and differentiate between corrective and preventive costs of quality assurance.

2. Discuss the breadth of a supervisor's responsibility for quality and list a number of ways to carry out this responsibility.

3. Describe the six principal reasons for errors and defects in employee performance and discuss the need for instilling a respect for quality among employees.

4. Understand the concepts and purpose of statistical quality control, make use of frequency-distribution and quality-control charts, and explain a reliability measure.

5. Describe the main features of zero-defects, quality circle, and total quality management programs and explain the value of participative approaches for solving quality problems.

CHAPTER STUDY GUIDE OUTLINES

Based on your study of the text chapter and/or your instructor's lesson presentation, complete the following outlines by supplying the correct answers for the numbered spaces. Some answers require more than one word to complete. Write the answers in the numbered answer column. Although you should rely principally on your recollection, you can use the textbook if you need help. Check your answers by referring to the keys at the back of this study guide.

▶ *Quality Assurance*

CONCEPT   Assurance of the quality of goods or services produced can be a costly process involving programs of inspection, correction, and prevention.

1. Quality is a measure of the degree to which a process, product, or service conforms to the requirements that have been established for it.

   Answers

   a. __(1)__ implies that all constituents in an enterprise must accept responsibility for the quality of goods and services that are linked to customer and client satisfaction.

   1. _____

   b. Quality assurance encompasses organizational efforts to assure that quality requirements are met.

   c. Quality control is similar to quality assurance but projects a __(2)__ connotation.

   2. _____

d. Inspection is a process of examination to discover the level of __(3)__ to or deviation from established requirements.

e. __(4)__ testing is inspection that doesn't break, distort, or otherwise damage the product (x-rays, sound waves, temperature flow patterns, magnetic fields, and so forth).

3. _____

4. _____

2. Quality control should be a concern of every line of work, not just manufacturing.

3. Poor quality costs industry __(5)__ of dollars annually.

a. Product liability and recalls are obvious costs.

b. Corrective costs equal __(6)__ of sales revenue.
   (1) Damaged parts and materials.
   (2) Time and effort of doing poor work over.
   (3) Cost of __(7)__ that presume errors will be made that must be corrected later.
   (4) Cost of handling customer complaints.

c. Preventive costs equal up to __(8)__ percent of sales revenue.
   (1) Inspection.
   (2) Testing.
   (3) Quality-control procedures including education and motivation programs.

5. _____

6. _____

7. _____

8. _____

▶ 2 Quality and the Supervisor

CONCEPT Supervisors have a major responsibility for making an organization's quality assurance effort successful.

1. The supervisor has a major, but __(9)__, responsibility for quality assurance.

a. Be clear that attainment of quality is not the responsibility of a single person or department.

b. Every __(10)__ of an organization contributes to, or detracts from, the quality of its products or services.
   (1) Often there is tension between the inspection and quality-control department and the supervisor's operators over who is the best __(11)__ of quality and who has the authority to stop production when quality falls below specifications.
      (a) The supervisor is pressured for output from __(12)__.
      (b) The quality-control department is pressured to ensure that output conforms to requirements.
   (2) Quality must be built __(13)__ the product. No one can inspect it in.

9. _____

10. _____

11. _____

12. _____

13. _____

2. Ten ideas to help establish quality checks are

   a. Set specific standards of quality; for example, dimensions and appearance.

   b. Give employees written quality specifications.

   c. Spend some __(14)__ time on inspection.   14. _____

   d. Inspect spots where quality problems are most serious or most likely to occur.

   e. Make inspection rounds on an __(15)__ schedule.   15. _____

   f. Inspect at random 5 to 10 percent of pieces produced at any station.

   g. Correct operating conditions __(16)__.   16. _____

   h. Consult employees to find reasons for poor quality.

   i. Check the __(17)__ piece of each setup.   17. _____

   j. Post quality records for the department.

▶ 3 Employee Contributions

      CONCEPT Employees can make or break a quality program, but they must first be given the proper information, training, and equipment.

1. Emphasize to employees from the first day, that quality and output go hand-in-hand.

2. Six reasons why employees make mistakes:

   a. Lack of training.

   b. Poor __(18)__.   18. _____

   c. Inadequate __(19)__ and equipment.   19. _____

   d. Insufficient planning.

   e. Incomplete specifications and procedures.

   f. Lack of attention or concern.

▶ 4 Statistical Quality Control

      CONCEPT Statistical quality control makes valuable use of mathematical techniques for monitoring and controlling the quality of processes, products, and services.

1. Statistical quality control (SQC) is the use of __(20)__   20. _____
(statistics) to control quality.

   a. The most frequently used methods include

      (1) Frequency-distribution charts (or histograms). These are tally cards. They help identify the __(21)__ of any variation (see text Figure 19–1).   21. _____

      (2) Quality-control chart. This provides a graphic comparison of product quality characteristics (see text Figure 19–2).

(3) __(22)__ tables. Statistical tables guide the quality-control manager and supervisor in determining how large a sample to take and how often to take it.

b. SQC considerations must take into account the limits of variation, or how far from standard the product can be __(23)__ being rejected.

22. _____

23. _____

5 ▶ *Toward Total Quality Management*

CONCEPT   The ultimate in quality achievement depends upon complete commitment and maximum participation by the entire organization.

1. Instead of a quality program that controls by __(24)__ work that doesn't measure up to minimum standards, the commitment to quality must involve every __(25)__ of the organization as well as constituents outside the enterprise.

24. _____

25. _____

2. The quality program called zero defects has had good results for three reasons:
   a. The quality standard is: Do it right from the start.
   b. Complete __(26)__ is needed from everyone.
   c. Action is taken __(27)__ to change behavior and remove conditions that cause errors. (Ninety percent of all error causes can be acted on and removed by first-line supervisors.)

26. _____

27. _____

3. Quality circles, conceived by Deming and used in Japan since the 1950s, are based on the belief that only by bringing together the people who are directly __(28)__ in the system will the obstacles that block good quality and error-free performance be removed.
   a. The concept of quality circles is based on maximum __(29)__ involvement of employees, meeting on company time.
   b. Quality circles need all-out support from top management.
   c. Facilitators help organize circles, and provide training in problem and opportunity identification and in methods improvement and problem solving.
   d. Personnel and __(30)__ problems are off limits, as are discussions about individual performance.
   e. Starting with __(31)__ workplace problems, circles use their growing expertise to attack more ambitious problems and later address problem prevention.

28. _____

29. _____

30. _____

31. _____

  f. Under current labor law in the United States, an employee team must function in a way that does not encroach upon __(32)__ prerogatives or employee rights to union representation and collective bargaining.

   (1) The quality circle should stick to __(33)__ problems involving quality and productivity and suggesting ways to improve them.

   (2) Team leaders and members should avoid appearing to represent or __(34)__ wages, hours of work, working conditions, or grievances.

  g. Circle success is based on common truths of motivation, group dynamics, Theory Y, and participation, which lead employees to try harder.

4. Total quality management is bigger than either zero defects or quality circles. See text Figure 19-3 for TQM's place in the quality-assurance evolution.

  a. It focuses on ultimate customer or client satisfaction, not only of the product or service, but also the manner in which all __(35)__ with the provider are conducted.

  b. The implementation of TQM typically involves some aspects of both zero defects and quality circles.

5. Benchmarking is much like TQM.

  a. A "__(36)__" benchmark begins with finding out exactly what customers and clients want in a product.

  b. "Competitor" or "external" benchmarks look at the way competitors and other companies provide their services, identify the best practice, and do it that way themselves.

  c. "__(37)__" benchmarks locate the place in the organization where a particular work activity is best performed and make that the benchmark or model for all departments performing similar work.

32. _____

33. _____

34. _____

35. _____

36. _____

37. _____

COMMENTARY ON SELF-APPRAISAL FROM THE TEXT

This self-appraisal is essentially a test of your understanding of the principles and practices discussed in the chapter. Some statements require reasoning before a choice can be made. And, as usual, there may be disagreement on some choices. If so, try to offer strong support for your choices.

  1. Good practice. The determination and/or knowledge of the specific quality standards are, of course, the foundation of all quality-assurance programs. Quality, to repeat, is a measurement of the degree to which processes, products, and services conform to established requirements.

2. Poor practice. Primary emphasis for quality assurance should be on preventive measures; they are less costly to implement, and they reduce the amount of corrective effort needed later on.

3. Good practice. Inspection does not put quality into the product or service; it must be built in. Inspection may be a necessary expense, but the supervisor's emphasis should be on quality performance first.

4. Poor practice. Supervisors should make their own spot checks and random inspections so that they are continually aware of quality progress in their operations. This does not replace or duplicate the worthwhile efforts of the formal inspections made under the supervision of the quality-control department.

5. Good practice. Supervisors should first ensure that the tools, equipment, and conditions necessary for quality performance are in place before making assumptions about employee error.

6. Poor practice. This item tests the student's understanding of why quality performance is so important. Its need goes far beyond a supervisor's domain. The ultimate quality boss is the customer—in the next department or to whom the product or service is sold.

7. Poor practice. The 100 percent inspections are extremely costly, especially on large batches of materials. Sampling techniques, using statistical quality-control methods, are far less costly—and surprisingly reliable.

8. Good practice. The effectiveness of statistical quality control for monitoring quality trends, where large quantities are involved, is stressed in the text's coverage of the subject.

9. Poor practice. Many of the ideas associated with zero defects are incorporated in quality circles—specific standards, commitment to excellence in quality, motivation, and participation in error removal.

10. Good practice. Increasingly, and as exemplified in quality circles, employee participation (or involvement) in identifying and helping to solve quality problems is a most effective approach.

SELF-CHECK OF YOUR PROGRESS

Part A: COMPLETION   An important term or phrase is needed to complete each of the following statements. Write the missing term in the space provided in the answer column.

Answers

1. The expense of handling customer complaints is an example of a(n) ____.

1. _____

2. The definition of expected performance expressed in terms of size, finish, shape, and so forth is a(n) ____.

2. _____

3. ____ is the quality-management technique based on finding the best product/service process or procedure and adopting it as the standard of quality performance.

3. _____

4. The limits within which the product or service must meet specifications are called the ____.

4. _____

5. ____ is using numbers as part of the overall approach for controlling quality.

5. _____

6. Modifying, adjusting, or making over a defective product is ____ .

7. The kind of performance that will be judged acceptable in terms of percentage of rejects, number of defects, number of customer complaints, and so forth is/are called ____ .

8. A variation from the specifications that cause the product to be rejected or reworked is a(n) ____ .

9. ____ is an inspection that does not break, distort, or damage the product being made.

10. ____ is the measure of the degree to which a process, product, or service conforms to the requirements that have been established for it.

6. _____

7. _____

8. _____

9. _____

10. _____

Part B: TRUE-FALSE   By writing T or F in the space provided, indicate whether each statement is true or false.

Answers

1. Quality problems are found in service organizations as well as manufacturing plants.

1. ____

2. It is unnecessary for employees to have written specifications about the quality of their work.

2. ____

3. Employees should understand that real quality control comes from the customer.

3. ____

4. The frequency-distribution chart is a commonly used quality-control tool.

4. ____

5. Tolerance is defined as a product's ability to perform a specific function, under given conditions for a specified time, without failure.

5. ____

6. Zero defects is an approach to quality control that emphasizes personal motivation.

6. ____

7. Quality circles stress that quality standards should be the primary responsibility of a single individual or department.

7. ____

8. As quality circles improve, they should take on the collective bargaining needs of an organization's employees.

8. ____

9. Zero defects has demonstrated that errors can be eliminated through sufficient personal motivation.

9. ____

10. If quality isn't built into a product, you must inspect it in.

10. ____

Part C: MULTIPLE CHOICE   Choose the response that best completes each statement. Write the letter of the response in the space provided.

1. Examples of preventive costs include
   a. Damaged parts that must be scrapped.
   b. Inspections.
   c. The time necessary to do poor work over.
   d. The cost of warranties.

Answers

1. ____

2. Which of the following statements most closely reflects the typical relationship between quality-control departments and production supervisors?
   a. Supervisors expect quality-control departments to handle quality issues.
   b. Since both the quality-control and production departments are concerned with quality, the quality-control department and the production supervisor tend to agree on quality issues.
   c. Disputes arise mainly over who is the best judge of quality.
   d. None of the above.

2. ____

3. Bonnie wants to improve her own quality checks. She should do all of the following, except
   a. Keep examples of acceptable and nonacceptable work on exhibit.
   b. Do some of the inspection herself.
   c. When substandard quality is found, correct operating conditions immediately.
   d. Let a new setup run for a while before her first quality check.   3. ___
4. Which of the following reasons that employees make errors is primarily their responsibility?
   a. Lack of training.
   b. Insufficient planning.
   c. Poor communications.
   d. Lack of attention.   4. ___
5. Seth has told his customer service staff that they should always answer the telephone within three rings. This is an example of
   a. Acceptable quality levels.
   b. Frequency-distribution charting.
   c. Tolerance.
   d. Reliability.   5. ___
6. Quality-control charts (QCC) differ from frequency-distribution charts (FDC) in that
   a. QCC is a statistical quality control.
   b. FDC can show tolerance variation.
   c. FDC can be used in manufacturing settings.
   d. QCC compares product quality over specific time frames.   6. ___
7. As a quality-control procedure, sampling tables are
   a. Less effective than spot checking.
   b. An aid to determine how large a sample to take and how often to take it.
   c. Produced by supervisors and adapted to their specific needs.
   d. Costly and misleading.   7. ___
8. Sweetness Toiletries expects its perfume to be bottled in 1-ounce bottles ± 0.001 ounce. This is an example of
   a. Radiography.
   b. Reliability.
   c. Tolerance.
   d. Inspection procedures.   8. ___
9. A customer warranty is an example of
   a. Reliability.
   b. Corrective cost.
   c. Preventive cost.
   d. Rework.   9. ___
10. The benchmarking practice of identifying the best there is in your field and doing it that way yourself, is an example of
    a. Customer benchmarking.
    b. Internal benchmarking.
    c. Competitor benchmarking.
    d. None of the above.   10. ___

CHAPTER 20 Managing a Diverse Workforce

LEARNING OBJECTIVES

After studying this chapter, you should be able to

1. Discuss the nature and workplace implications of a culturally diverse society.

2. Identify and interpret the major equal employment opportunity legislation, explain the intent of affirmative action plans, and describe the role of the Equal Employment Opportunity Commission.

3. Discuss the special problems of disadvantaged workers and suggest ways for integrating these employees successfully into the workplace.

4. Discuss the importance of women in the workplace and their difficulties in advancing from their traditional roles, including related subjects such as job evaluation, comparable worth, and sexual harassment.

5. Discuss the unique assets and drawbacks of aging workers.

6. Explain the legal and social aspects of an employee's right to privacy and the impact this has on a supervisor's right to manage.

CHAPTER STUDY GUIDE OUTLINES

Based on your study of the text chapter and/or your instructor's lesson presentation, complete the following outlines by supplying the correct answers for the numbered spaces. Some answers require more than one word to complete. Write the answers in the numbered answer column. Although you should rely principally on your recollection, you can use the textbook if you need help. Check your answers by referring to the keys at the back of this study guide.

▶ A Diverse Workforce

CONCEPT Society and our resultant workforce is becoming more culturally diverse every year.

1. There are dramatic changes being made in the United States workforce.
   a. In 1985, 47 percent of the labor force were native-born white men.

b. By the year __(1)__, new workers in the labor force will have changed significantly. Of the new workers
  (1) 15 percent will be native-born white men.
  (2) 42 percent will be native-born white women.
  (3) 7 percent will be native-born nonwhite men.
  (4) 13 percent nonwhite women.
  (5) 13 percent __(2)__ men.
  (6) 9 percent immigrant women.

c. The number of young workers age 16–24 will drop 8 percent.

d. 61 percent of all women of working age will have __(3)__.

e. 29 percent of all new job holders will be nonwhite, __(4)__ their current representation in the work-force.

2. Good supervisors will seek a workforce reflective of these changes in the labor pool.

a. They will also recognize there are cultural differences between ethnic and racial groups that must be understood in order to be an effective supervisor.

b. Participation in cultural awareness and cultural __(5)__ workshops can give supervisors a better understanding of the range of people they will encounter as employees.

3. In addition to race and gender differences, supervisors should be aware of the differences that can be the result of marital status, disability, age, __(6)__, veteran's status, or religious belief.

4. It is not the supervisor's responsibility to have an opinion on the __(7)__ of the differences they will see in their workforce.

a. Pay attention to work __(8)__.

b. Part of successfully managing people is understanding their needs and focusing their attention on work goals and objectives.

Answers

1. _____

2. _____

3. _____

4. _____

5. _____

6. _____

7. _____

8. _____

▶ 2 The Legal Basis

CONCEPT A strong body of law establishes the rights and privileges of all job applicants and employees regardless of race, color, national origin, gender, disability, or age.

1. Basic equal employment opportunity (EEO) laws state that an employer cannot __(9)__ against a member of a protected group because of race, color, religion, gender, national origin, disability, or age.

9. _____

    a. Protected groups include blacks, Hispanics, Asians, Native Americans, women, disadvantaged young persons, Vietnam-era veterans, and persons over __(10)__ years of age.

    b. EEO laws are the direct expression of the public's dissatisfaction and its wish to change extreme poverty, discrimination, and second-class employment treatment of some groups.

2. The legal basis for EEO programs is a great body of federal, state, and local laws; significant court rulings and legal interpretations; and __(11)__ laid down by the Equal Employment Opportunity Commission (EEOC). (See text Table 20–1.) In summary, these laws specify that most firms and public institutions cannot

    a. Make any distinctions based on race, gender, or national origin in any condition of __(12)__, including hiring, paying wages (equal pay for equal work), classifying, assigning or promoting, and allocating the use of facilities, and in training, retraining, and apprenticeship programs.

    b. Distinguish between married and single people of one sex and not the other.

    c. Deny employment to women with young children unless the same policies apply to __(13)__ with young children.

    d. Penalize women because they may require time from work for __(14)__.

    e. Maintain seniority lists based solely on gender or race.

    f. Establish jobs as men's or women's unless the employer can show there is a __(15)__.

    g. Discriminate against workers 40 years of age or older in hiring, firing, promoting, classifying, paying, assigning, advertising, or setting eligibility requirements for union membership.

    h. Similarly discriminate against qualified __(16)__ persons. Persons with disabilities (some prefer "differently abled") are defined as

      (1) Having a physical or mental impairment.

      (2) Having a record of such impairments.

      (3) Being regarded as having such impairments.

3. EEOC and its state and local equivalents have encouraged the use of __(17)__ programs—positive written action plans to ensure nondiscriminatory treatment of all protected groups.

10. _____

11. _____

12. _____

13. _____

14. _____

15. _____

16. _____

17 _____

a. Companies with federal contracts over $50,000 and with more than 50 employees are required to have a plan.

b. Companies with poor records of treatment or employment of protected groups can be directed to set up a plan.

4. Investigation of discrimination by the EEOC will focus on

a. Differential treatment.

b. __(18)__ effect—job requirements that exclude a protected group unless a BFOQ exists.

c. Evil intent.

5. Reverse discrimination is what many people believe happens to men and whites when preference is shown to protected groups.

a. In the Bakke case, the Supreme Court ruled in effect that it was wrong to use quotas to withhold employment from eligible men and whites.

b. At the same time, the Court upheld the principle of affirmative action.

6. Americans With Disabilitiy Act of 1990 (ADA) prohibits discrimination in all employment practices, and it includes private employers with __(19)__ or more employees and all state and local governments.

a. According to ADA, a person who has a physical or mental impairment that substantially limits one or more major __(20)__, has a record of such impairment, or is regarded as having such an impairment, is defined as an individual with a disability.

(1) If persons with a disability meet the job requirements and can perform the essential functions of that job, they should be accepted as candidates for employment without considering their __(21)__.

(2) If hired, the employer is expected to make reasonable accommodations to a job or work environment to enable them to perform the essential job functions.

(a) An employer is __(22)__ required to make accommodations if it imposes an undue hardship on the business.

(b) Most accommodations are possible within the economic resources of most employers.

18. _____

19. _____

20. _____

21. _____

22. _____

(3) ADA also requires that physical barriers to __(23)__ be removed when readily achievable.

23. _____

7. The Family and Medical Leave Act (FMLA) of 1993 permits eligible employees to take up to 12 weeks of __(24)__ leave per 12-month period for the birth or care of a child, the placement of a child for adoptive or foster care, to care for an immediate family member if that family member has a serious health condition, or in response to a serious health condition that makes the employee unable to perform the functions of his or her position.

24. _____

   a. After completing the leave, the employee __(25)__ be restored to his or her former or equivalent position.

25. _____

   b. FMLA does not supersede state laws or collective bargaining agreements that require more generous leave policies.

3▶ *Disadvantaged Minorities*

CONCEPT   A significant part of the population has traditionally been "disadvantaged" and requires especially supportive treatment from their supervisors.

1. The hard-core unemployed are out of work more than they are employed. Typically, they have the following characteristics:
   a. They are school __(26)__ , usually in the sixth or seventh grade, with poor English and arithmetic skills.

26. _____

   b. They are heads of households.
   c. They have a poor work history.
   d. They are plagued with __(27)__ problems.

2. To avoid earlier problems with discriminatory job testing (*Griggs v. Duke Power*, 1971), federal guidelines require that tests be validated to prove that they measure what they say they measure and don't exclude people in a discriminatory fashion. Tests must have

27. _____

   a. Content validity—the test is related to job requirements.
   b. __(28)__ validity—the test shouldn't screen out applicants who could pass the test if they could only understand the questions themselves.

28. _____

4 ▸ Women in the Workplace

CONCEPT   Women have traditionally been denied equal opportunities in the workplace, and their rights must now be protected and enhanced.

1. Forty percent of all jobs are held by women; they hold more than 40 percent of all managerial and professional jobs and nearly two-thirds of all technical, sales, and administrative support jobs.

2. The percentage of working women has increased regularly (see text Figure 20–1).

3. Women have traditionally had lower-paying, lower-status jobs and have been blocked from __(29)__ into higher ones; this has resulted in the average pay for females being about two thirds to three-quarters of the average pay for men.

   29. _____

   a. Federal law stipulates that all employees within a firm should receive the same __(30)__ for the same kind and amount of work.

   30. _____

   b. Job evaluation is the basic internal means to ensure that these federal laws are enforced, with special attention paid to equal skill, effort, responsibility, and working conditions. The laws do permit pay differences based on merit and seniority.

   c. __(31)__ extends the concept of equal pay for equal work (Equal Pay Act, 1963) to the evaluation of the worth of jobs (within an organization) that may be radically different from each other.

   31. _____

    (1) Comparable worth involves evaluation and comparison of the level of know-how required, problem solving entailed, accountability, and working conditions.

4. Many women are concerned that the labor market does not provide equal opportunity to secure intellectually challenging jobs and a chance to advance in __(32)__ to their performance and capabilities.

   32. _____

5. There should be no major differences in how women and men are __(33)__ .

   33. _____

6. The fact that women successfully hold jobs in every occupational classification should illustrate the speciousness of withholding from any woman the opportunity to perform the kind of work for which she may be qualified.

7. __(34)__ is a serious employment issue.

   34. _____

   a. It is defined by the EEOC as unwelcome sexual advances, requests for sexual favors, and other verbal or physical conduct of a sexual nature when

   (1) Submission to such conduct is made either explicitly or implicitly a term or condition of an individual's employment.

   (2) Submission to or rejection of such conduct by an individual is used as the basis for employment decisions.

   (3) Conduct has the purpose or effect of unreasonably interfering with an individual's work performance by creating an intimidating, hostile, or offensive working environment.

b. The supervisor has a crucial role preventing and responding to complaints of sexual harassment.

   (1) You must know who will conduct the __(35)__.   35. _____

   (2) Be sure to document all actions that you take.

   (3) It is important that appropriate discipline, up to and including termination, be considered.

   (4) Remember sexual harassment is primarily about __(36)__, not sex.   36. _____

   (5) Reputable national studies suggest more than 50 percent of all women in the workforce, at some point in their work life, have been __(37)__ of sexual harassment.   37. _____

c. Supervisors can help prevent harassment of their employees by

   (1) Stating clearly that you will not __(38)__ sexual   38. _____
   harassment, and cases reported to you will be investigated completely and, if proven, dealt with severely.

   (2) Review your physical environment and don't tolerate "locker-room pin-ups," offensive humor, and physical sexual intimidation.

   (3) Encourage employees to __(39)__ acts of sexual   39. _____
   harassment they experience or overhear.

5 ▶ Younger and Older Workers

   CONCEPT   Younger, as well as older, workers require a special kind of nurturing from their supervisors.

1. Characteristics that distinguish typical younger workers include

   a. A deep preoccupation with themselves as individuals with unique prerogatives.

   b. Almost universal __(40)__ of everything traditional.   40. _____

2. Characteristics that distinguish disadvantaged younger workers are
   a. An outlook that recognizes no values beyond today.
   b. A disbelief in the possibility that business will ever provide an honest opportunity to succeed.
   c. A hopeless feeling that the cards are stacked against them.
3. Younger workers are more likely than older workers to __(41)__ or to leave an unsatisfying job.

41. _____

4. Supervisors can improve the motivation and management of younger workers if they
   a. Exert authority only from reason.
   b. Learn to move faster in making __(42)__.

42. _____

   c. Convey the meaning of each assignment.
   d. Make sure the younger workers know what results are expected of them.
   e. Provide support and assistance.
   f. __(43)__ freely when deserved.

43. _____

   g. Enrich the nature of work.
5. The Age Discrimination Employment Act applies to workers over 40 years of age. However,
   a. Age affects each individual differently.
   b. Supervisors will notice more age-related changes in employees over 50 years of age.
6. The chief assets of older workers include safety, attendance, judgment, loyalty, and skill.
   a. Oftentimes, an older worker has a wealth of experience to draw upon and is skilled with
      (1) Various office __(44)__.

44. _____

      (2) General office procedure.
      (3) Preparing reports, documents, and correspondence.
      (4) Working with the public (in person and by telephone).
7. The chief drawbacks of older workers are that they may be slower, weaker, and less resilient, and may suffer from poor eyesight.
8. Older workers learn as quickly as younger workers if they are well motivated, especially if kept well appraised of how they are doing.
9. Older workers have the most difficulty learning a new skill if the skill __(45)__ with what they have already learned.

45. _____

   a. Help them to be less critical and less self-conscious.
   b. Keep performance standards high.

6 ▸ *Special Problems in a Changing Environment*

CONCEPT   Changes in both the social and legal environments create special problems of supervision in handling sensitive issues of privacy and other employee rights.

1. Laws regarding an employee's right to privacy vary from state to state. In general,
   a. Employees are entitled to know what information is __(46)__ about them.

   46. _____

   b. Supervisors are restricted in the efforts to find out confidential information concerning an employee or to pass confidential information on to others outside the company.

2. Invasions of an employee's privacy include
   a. Monitoring or recording __(47)__ without consent.

   47. _____

   b. Using extraordinary means—for example, calling a neighbor—to check on absences or off-job behavior.
   c. Making random __(48)__ through lockers or personal space at work.

   48. _____

   d. __(49)__ information to an outside organization without permission.

   49. _____

3. __(50)__ tests are acceptable if needed to protect the business or customers from damage or theft.

   50. _____

4. A supervisor's duties are more complicated because of concerns for protected groups and privacy; however, their duties can be handled successfully if the supervisors remember
   a. First things should come first.
      (1) Deal promptly and firmly with subordinates whose performance is unsatisfactory, unsafe, uncooperative, or abusive.
      (2) This is consistent with management and labor relations law and most employees' expectations.
   b. Full attention and respect should be given to EEO laws and other legislation intended to protect the rights and welfare of people at work.
   c. Supervisors need to maintain an attitude of accommodation to social concerns like family leaves, __(51)__ , and parental assistance programs.

   51. _____

5. Privacy, to a large extent, is extended to sensitive issues like AIDS. Supervisors should
   a. Rely on policies adopted by their __(52)__ and comply with them.

   52. _____

b. Support the letter of whatever law applies and company policies for implementing those laws.

c. Recognize that it is now clear that those suffering from this disease can have long, __(53)__ work lives.

53. _____

d. Be prepared to offer reasonable accommodations should changes in the illness require them.

e. If other employees express concerns about AIDS, get the __(54)__ about the illness and share them with your employees.

54. _____

COMMENTARY ON SELF-APPRAISAL FROM THE TEXT

This self-appraisal requires a high degree of interpretation by you, especially when compared with simply memorizing the stipulations in the various EEO laws. The gender identifications for some roles are switched, for example. This forces you to think through the intent of the EEO legislation, which is to protect equal employment opportunity rights for everyone, regardless of gender, race, age, and so forth.

1. Special considerations regarding child care must be extended to employees of both sexes, or neither. The fact that the mother is unmarried is not a factor.

2. Providing equal opportunity for training is an essential part of EEO law.

3. This violates the mandate that jobs cannot be classified as either men's or women's, nor can seniority lists be maintained on that basis.

4. You may regard this as marginal, but affirmative action implies that special efforts be made to accommodate language and cultural handicaps of disadvantaged workers like Mannie.

5. So long as the content and construct validity of employment tests are met, their use does not deny any applicant his or her equal employment opportunities. A major reason for using employment tests is to separate the qualified from the unqualified candidates on an unbiased basis.

6. An approved job-evaluation plan helps to assure that jobs are classified—and compensated—on a systematic, objective, unbiased basis.

7. If the heavy work is assigned to all employees—and thus can be assumed to be a part of the job requirements for everybody—then making an exception for an employee, whether man or woman, denies others their equal opportunity rights. Moreover, what most women want is equal treatment in the workplace, with neither favor nor disfavor.

8. This practice follows the EEO mandate that there be no discrimination in assigning or promoting employees. When job openings are made known to everyone and everyone is given an opportunity to present his or her credentials, this conforms to part of the prescribed EEO and affirmative action procedures.

9. Young workers perform better when they understand why something must be done in a certain way or why they must conform to an unpleasant routine.

10. Older workers learn faster when they are helped to relate new ways to old, familiar ones.

11. Workers with disabilities are members of a protected group (Rehabilitation Act of 1973 and Executive Order 11914 of 1974), and must (if the firm is a federal contractor) be given an equal opportunity to show whether they are qualified to perform the work available. Pearl's action would be judged as disparate effect.

12. A vestibule training area gives an employee an opportunity to learn the job away from the pressure for real time performance. This is certainly in line with the consideration that EEOC urges for disadvantaged workers.

13. This action is in direct opposition to the Americans With Disability Act (ADA). In most cases, remodeling of a restroom would be seen by nearly every unbiased observer to be a reasonable accommodation and something an employer should do for an otherwise qualified applicant.

14. Pearl is violating EEO legislation by prejudicing and stereotyping, and thus is discriminating against Alice.

15. This statement is not true. The Family Medical Leave Act (FMLA) provides leaves for placement of a child with an employee for adoption or foster care.

SELF-CHECK OF YOUR PROGRESS

Part A: COMPLETION   An important term or phrase is needed to complete each of the following statements. Write the missing term in the space provided in the answer column.

Answers

1. A ____ consists of people who historically have encountered discrimination in the workplace and have warranted special legislative protection.

1. _____

2. A ____ can be used to reserve a job just for men or just for women.

2. _____

3. ____ programs consist of positive action taken to ensure nondiscriminatory treatment of all groups protected by legislation forbidding employment discrimination.

3. _____

4. ____ occurs when a protected group member is treated differently from a nonmember in the same situation.

4. _____

5. ____ occurs when a job requirement acts to exclude a member of a protected group.

5. _____

6. When qualified nonprotected class members are deprived of employment opportunities because of an affirmative action program, they sometimes allege ____

6. _____

7. A supervisor could be charged with ____ if he or she makes sexually explicit remarks that are offensive to the recipient.

7. _____

8. ____ means that the test content is truly related to the job requirements.

8. _____

9. ____ means that the test is put together in a way which doesn't screen out applicants who could pass the content part if only they could understand the test questions.

9. _____

10. ____ is the concept of evaluating widely dissimilar jobs for the purpose of providing equal pay for jobs of similar worth to the organization.

10. _____

Part B: TRUE-FALSE   By writing T or F in the space provided, indicate whether each statement is true or false.

Answers

1. Cultural diversity workshops can give supervisors suggestions for managing the range of people they will encounter in the workforce.

1. ___

2. The Civil Rights Act prohibits discrimination in employment based on gender, race, or national origin.

2. ___

3. According to federal legislation, an employer may distinguish between married and single people of one sex and not the other.

3. ___

4. The Age Discrimination Act, as amended in 1975, prohibits discriminating against workers 40 to 64 years old.

4. ___

5. An employee or candidate for work who suffers from an inferior education is an example of a disadvantaged worker.

5. ___

6. The hard-core unemployed are members of the workforce who are temporarily out of a job.

6. ___

7. Women do not have the right to return to their old job after returning from childbirth.

7. ___

8. According to ADA, an employer is expected to make reasonable accommodations to a job to enable a qualified applicant or employee with a disability to perform the essential job functions.

8. ___

9. Older workers learn best when they are kept apprised of how well they are doing.

9. ___

10. After completing a leave covered by The Family and Medical Leave Act, employees must be restored to their former position or an equivalent position.

10. ___

Part C: MULTIPLE CHOICE   Choose the response that best completes each statement. Write the letter of the response in the space provided.

1. The public's general dissatisfaction with discrimination has resulted in
   a. The economic necessity of women working outside of the home.
   b. Changing values brought about by different family lifestyles and marriage patterns.
   c. Lack of patience in many people.
   d. Current equal opportunity legislation.

Answers

1. ___

2. Executive Orders 11246 and 11375
   a. Prohibit discrimination in firms sharing government contracts of more than $10,000.
   b. Require men and women to be paid equally for the same amount of work.
   c. Prohibit union and employment agencies from discriminating in hiring.
   d. Prohibit discrimination in training and retraining.   2. ____

3. The Civil Rights Act as amended prohibits discrimination in
   a. Employment for firms having government contracts of over $10,000.
   b. Employment for firms having government contracts of over $25,000.
   c. The location of business expansions.
   d. Hiring employees.   3. ____

4. Reverse discrimination is discrimination against
   a. Hispanics.
   b. Blacks.
   c. Women.
   d. Nonminorities.   4. ____

5. A supervisor can help prevent the sexual harassment of his or her employees by
   a. Clearly stating that he or she will not tolerate sexual harassment.
   b. Encouraging employees to report acts of sexual harassment they experience or overhear.
   c. Ensuring that any case reported to him or her will be investigated completely and if proven, dealt with severely.
   d. All of the above.   5. ____

6. Most women miss (on their jobs or at the workplace) the opportunity
   a. To compete with men.
   b. For intellectually challenging work.
   c. To prove their ability.
   d. To demonstrate loyalty to company objectives.   6. ____

7. A supervisor can better motivate and manage young workers by
   a. Using an autocratic leadership style.
   b. Not allowing change to occur too swiftly.
   c. Conveying the meaning of each assignment.
   d. Being careful not to overpraise.   7. ____

8. The unemployment rate is highest for
   a. Black workers.
   b. Women workers.
   c. Younger workers.
   d. Older workers.   8. ____

9. The discovery by EEOC that an employer would not hire Hispanic workers is most likely to result in a finding of
   a. Disparate effect.
   b. Evil intent.
   c. Reverse discrimination.
   d. Differential treatment.   9. ____

10. One of the chief drawbacks of older workers is
    a. They have far more accidents on the job.
    b. Their attendance record is lower than other employees.
    c. They have less endurance than they once had.
    d. They are likely to have poorer judgment than other employees.

    10. ____

CHAPTER

21 Employee Safety and Health Under OSHA

LEARNING OBJECTIVES

After studying this chapter, you should be able to

1. Discuss the extensive list of factors in addition to human error that contribute to occupational injuries and illnesses.

2. Explain various facets of the Occupational Safety and Health Act and its enforcement.

3. Evaluate several common approaches to accident prevention—including the three E's of engineering, education, and enforcement—and discuss the effectiveness of safety clothing, safety posters, and safety committees.

4. Identify the most common types of occupational accidents and the places where they occur, and describe several ways for preventing each.

5. Compute occupational accident incident and severity rates, and understand the procedures for investigating and analyzing an accident.

Chapter Study Guide Outlines

Based on your study of the text chapter and/or your instructor's lesson presentation, complete the following outlines by supplying the correct answers for the numbered spaces. Some answers require more than one word to complete. Write the answers in the numbered answer column. Although you should rely principally on your recollection, you can use the textbook if you need help. Check your answers by referring to the keys at the back of this study guide.

1▶ Safety at Work

CONCEPT   Accidents and hazards to health represent costly factors in the work environment and must be guarded against constantly.

Answers

1. __(1)__ can be prevented by people taking proper protective or control action.

   a. Ninety-one percent of accidents can be attributed to __(2)__ acts.

   b. Nine percent of accidents are caused by environmental factors or faulty equipment.

1. _____

2. _____

2. Work-related accidents cost industry nearly __(3)__ annually and the cost is rising, but the human costs are even greater.
   a. More than 10,000 workers in the United States are __(4)__ every year.
   b. Six million workers, per year, are injured on the job.
3. Only a very small percentage of employees are truly accident prone.
4. Commonly recognized causes of accidents (other than employee carelessness or inattention) include
   a. The absence of, or faulty, protective devices.
   b. Ineffective specifications for safety clothing.
   c. The presence of hazardous or unauthorized materials.
   d. The __(5)__ tools, materials, or supplies issued to the job.
   e. The absence of a safety standard for the operation.
   f. The lack of safety training for a specific task.
   g. Inadequate or improper instructions.
   h. Safety rules or procedures not being enforced.
   i. Assignment of a person to a task to which he or she is unsuited.
   j. Poor housekeeping or sanitation at the workplace.
   k. Pressure from __(6)__ to disregard safe procedures in the interest of faster movement or greater output.

3. _____

4. __ _____

5. _____

6. _____

2 ▶ *OSHA's Mandated Safety Standards*

CONCEPT The federal government establishes and monitors (through OSHA) strict standards for protection of safety and health at work.

1. Since the passage of the Williams-Steiger Occupational Safety and Health Act (1970), the federal government, through the Occupational Safety and Health Administration (OSHA), has been directly involved in safety issues in every significant plant and office in the United States.
   a. OSHA establishes __(7)__ standards with which every employer and employee must comply.
   b. It makes more than 100,000 safety __(8)__ annually.
   c. National Consensus Standards specify nearly everything imaginable, with particular attention to paper, textile, laundry, sawmill, and bakery operations. The standards are regularly revised, updated, and published in the Federal Register.

7. _____

8. _____

2. Failure to comply with OSHA standards will result in a __(9)__ issued to a manager or supervisor, followed by a penalty and fine if corrective action isn't taken.

9. _____

3. OSHA goes beyond safety and monitors employee health, with particular attention to sanitation and hazardous materials.

4. OSHA has made ongoing safety training __(10)__.

10. _____

5. Each employee is required to comply with safety and health standards, rules, and orders.

6. Employee rights under OSHA include the right to

   a. Request an __(11)__.

11. _____

   b. Have a representative accompany the OSHA compliance officer during the inspection.

   c. Question and be questioned in private by the compliance officer concerning any violations the employees believe exist.

   d. Have regulations posted to inform employees of protections afforded by the act.

   e. Have locations monitored for toxic or radioactive materials and review monitoring records, including a record of the employees' own personal exposure.

   f. Have medical examinations and tests to see if the health of the employees has been affected by an exposure and furnish the test results to their physicians.

   g. Have any employer citations __(12)__ on the premises.

12. _____

3 ▶ Accident Prevention: the Basics

CONCEPT Supervisors play the key role in accident prevention by emphasizing safety awareness, education, and enforcement.

1. Good __(13)__ is the starting place for an effective accident prevention program. Take the safety lead and

13. _____

   a. Instill the belief that employees are the most __(14)__ source of accident prevention.

14. _____

      (1) Discuss the details of __(15)__ that have occurred.

15. _____

      (2) Let employees know the cause and effect of accidents

   b. Show employees how to develop safe working habits.

c. Pay special attention to __(16)__ employees.

d. Be specific about prevention techniques.

e. Enlist safety __(17)__ from employees.

f. Set a good example.

g. Firmly __(18)__ safety job standards.

2. The National Safety Council stresses the three E's of accident prevention: __(19)__, education, and enforcement (see text Figure 21–1).

3. Safety specialists are important, but safety programs, especially education and enforcement, would flop without the __(20)__.

4. Employees will wear safety clothing if trained to do their work in it, if they understand how it protects them, and if everybody expects them to wear it.

a. Let them help decide what kind of __(21)__ fits the situation best.

b. Offer a selection.

c. Set an __(22)__ yourself.

d. Get help from the informal leaders in the work group.

e. Show that you mean business.

5. Don't __(23)__ the value of safety posters. They help a little but the big job is up to you.

6. Safety committees are more useful if you

a. Assign the committee specific problems.

b. __(24)__ results.

c. Have members participate on investigations.

d. Delegate duties.

16. _____

17. _____

18. _____

19. _____

20. _____

21. _____

22. _____

23. _____

24. _____

◢4 *Accident Prevention: the Specifics*

CONCEPT   There are a number of good ways to prevent the most common accidents, such as those involving lifting, falling, machinery, hand tools, electricity, and fires.

1. Accidents happen most frequently and are most severe in manufacturing, mining, food processing, construction, transportation, and the __(25)__ business; they are least frequent in banks and insurance companies (see text Figure 21–2).

2. Most industrial accidents on the job occur

a. Around hand lift trucks, wheelbarrows, warehouses, cranes, and shipping departments. Nearly one-third of industrial accidents are caused by handling and lifting materials.

b. Near metal, woodworking, and transmission machinery.

25. _____

   c. On stairs, ladders, walkways, and scaffolds.

   d. Anywhere hand tools are used—they cause 7 percent of industrial disability.

   e. Everywhere __(26)__ is used.

   26. _____

3. Remember, even in industrial settings, accidents can be prevented.

   a. DuPont Company has 100,000 employees and manufactures explosives and heavy chemicals.

   b. The DuPont lost-time incident rate is .04 when the national average for their industry is over 70.0.

4. __(27)__ office workers are injured annually. Many office accidents

   27. _____

   a. Occur in normal work areas and stockrooms.

   b. Occur because office equipment is out of place.

   c. Result from __(28)__ hazards that induce repetitive strain injuries.

   28. _____

   d. Are caused by common items found in the office, for example, a swivel chair that tips over or a piece of paper that gives a paper cut.

5. Lifting and material-handling accidents can be prevented by

   a. Lifting with your __(29)__ rather than your back.

   29. _____

   b. Keeping loads light or getting help lifting.

   c. Keeping floors and aisles clean.

   d. Not overloading mechanical lifting devices.

   e. Training inexperienced workers how to use mechanical equipment first.

6. Machinery, machine tools, and power-transmission equipment accidents (these result in the most severe injuries) can be reduced by

   a. Inspecting all new tools before they are __(30)__.

   30. _____

   b. Cautioning employees about wearing __(31)__ clothing near machines.

   31. _____

   c. Observing employees until you are sure they know the danger a machine holds and how to avoid accidents.

   d. Making sure employees know how to shut down machines quickly.

7. To prevent falls, keep an eye out for

   a. Unsafe floors and work surfaces.

   b. Unsafe ladders, stairways, and scaffolds.

   c. Improper __(32)__.

   32. _____

   d. Unsafe practices.

   e. Inadequate lighting.

8. To prevent hand-tool accidents
   a. Throw away or repair tools in bad shape.
   b. Always have the right tool for the job available and use it.
   c. Be sure employees are __(33)__ to use all tools.
   d. Follow the tool manufacturer's guide for safe use.

33. _____ _____

9. To prevent low-voltage (anything under 600 volts) electric shocks
   a. Require the __(34)__ of all hot wires, tingling shocks, abnormal sparking, frayed insulation, loose connections, and so forth.
   b. Have the plant electrician investigate quickly.
   c. Ground power hand tools.
   d. Don't let employees disconnect fuses, circuit breakers, and similar protective devices.
   e. If an accident occurs, remove the employee from the electrical source and give artificial respiration.

34. _____ _____

10. To prevent __(35)__
    a. Keep areas clean and neat.
    b. Keep materials away from sprinklers, extinguishers, and hoses.
    c. Be sure the fire-fighting equipment is operating and use it only to fight fires.
    d. Don't be lenient about __(36)__ in unauthorized areas.
    e. Regard every open flame, match, cigarette, bit of oily waste, and drop of flammable liquid as potentially dangerous.

35. _____

36. _____

11. In case of fire, immediately
    a. Report the fire to the company or local fire department.
    b. __(37)__ employees.
    c. Use a hand extinguisher or hose.

37. _____

5▶ Accident Reporting and Investigation

CONCEPT   Accident prevention also depends on rigorous measurement, reporting, investigation, and analysis of the causes of accidents.

1. OSHA requires that every company maintain a log of illnesses and accidents as they occur.
   a. __(38)__ records whether each illness or injury caused a fatality, lost workday, permanent transfer, or termination.

38. _____

b. In the area of illness identification, OSHA requires a report on occupational skin diseases and disorders, dust diseases of the lungs, respiratory conditions and poisoning, disorders due to other physical agents, and traumas.

c. Companies are required to keep specialized records, including inspection and maintenance __(39)__, on scaffolding, platforms, man lifts, fire extinguishers, cranes, derricks, and power presses.

39. _____

d. Companies are required to keep records for radiation exposure, flammable and combustible liquids inventories, and logs of toxic and hazardous substances.

2. OSHA and the U.S. Bureau of Labor Statistics determine what constitutes an __(40)__ (or accident case) and how to measure the incident rate (frequency rate) and severity rate.

40. _____

a. A recordable incident involves occupational injury or illness, including death.

b. Not recordable incidents are first-time ailments involving one-time treatments, minor cuts, scratches, or burns that ordinarily don't require __(41)__, even if such treatment was provided by a physician or nurse.

41. _____

c. Accident rates (incident and severity rates) are measured by a general formula that relates cases (incident rate) or lost __(42)__ (severity rate) to the time of 100 workers working 2,000 hours per year, or a total of 200,000 hours.

42. _____

$$\text{Incident rate (Frequency rate)} = \frac{\text{no. of recordable cases} \times 200{,}000 \text{ hours}}{\text{total hours worked by all employees during the year}}$$

$$\text{Severity rate} = \frac{\text{no. of workdays lost} \times 200{,}000 \text{ hours}}{\text{total hours worked by all employees during the year}}$$

3. Accident investigation uncovers what happened and what can be done to __(43)__ the problem in the future. It should answer the following questions:

43. _____

a. What happened?

b. Why did it happen?

c. What needs to be done to prevent it from happening again?

d. What steps have been taken to prevent recurrence?

e. What still needs to be __(44)__?

44. _____

4. Insurance and workers' compensation don't cover all accident costs.
   a. Liability insurance costs are related to a company's safety record.
   b. For every $1,000 of compensation paid, it is estimated a company pays __(45)__ in related expenses, such as time lost to watch, assist, and investigate the accident; the cost in time and labor to change production schedules, assign and train new workers; the cost of medical care; and so forth.

   45. _____

5. Only trained people should provide __(46)__ to the patient.
   a. Summon medical help quickly.
   b. Stay with the employee until he or she is under medical care.

   46. _____

6. Safety and sanitation inspections are an essential part of an accident prevention and control program. They should
   a. Be conducted regularly.
   b. Be based upon verifying __(47)__ with the company's and OSHA's rules and standards.
   c. Seek to detect new areas of necessary coverage.
   d. Be followed up quickly by rigorous __(48)__ action.

   47. _____

   48. _____

7. The most common wellness programs are smoking control, health-risk assessment, __(49)__, stress management, exercise and physical fitness, off-the-job accident prevention, nutrition education, blood-pressure control, and weight control.
   a. The effectiveness of these programs is debated.
   b. They are not as __(50)__ with employees as was once expected.

   49. _____

   50. _____

COMMENTARY ON SELF-APPRAISAL FROM THE TEXT

This self-appraisal represents a balanced assortment of questions directly related to material presented in the chapter. Only an occasional item can be challenged. If so, be prepared to cite the support for a contrary position.

1. False. The text makes specific mention of the unmeasurable costs of accidents in terms of pain and damaged lives.

2. False. The text reports that psychologists maintain that even employees with poor accident histories can be trained to avoid them in the future. The main approach used in accomplishing this is behavior modification—a system of rewards (praise)

for good behavior and penalties (or no praise or attention) for unsatisfactory behavior. Chapter 13, "Counseling Troubled Employees," discusses behavior modification or reinforcement theory in greater detail.

3. False. Although most accidents can be traced to human error, they are not always the result of error on the part of the person who is injured.

4. True. This is clearly the case.

5. False. OSHA standards were derived from those of the American National Standards Institute (ANSI), the National Fire Protection Association (NFPA), and established federal standards, which appeared in previous, but related, legislation.

6. True. This is clearly stated in the text.

7. False. OSHA stipulates that employees must conform to established standards, provided that the employer has fulfilled its responsibilities.

8. False. The third phase is enforcement, not evaluation.

9. False. Safety specialists can play an important role in accident prevention programs, but accidents occur—and are prevented—by education (communication, training, and motivation) and enforcement provided by first-line supervisors.

10. True. The prescribed safety clothing must be worn, of course, but participation in its selection is an effective way to ensure that it will be worn.

11. False. Check the text: safety committees should have serious, active responsibilities rather than solely passive, advisory roles.

12. False. There are two other actions to be considered—calling the fire department and getting employees out of the area. Many authorities believe that employees should be evacuated as soon as the alarm is sounded and that it is dangerous to try to fight the fire before the alarm is sounded or before employees are evacuated.

13. True. Review the material in the text for clarity.

14. False. A recordable incident (or case) includes illnesses as well as disabling accidents and does not require that days be lost to be so considered.

15. False. Workers' compensation is compensation or an award for an injury that permanently restricts an employee's earning capacity.

SELF-CHECK OF YOUR PROGRESS

Part A: COMPLETION An important term or phrase is needed to complete each of the following statements. Write the missing term in the space provided in the answer column.

Answers

1. ____ makes over 100,000 inspections annually and establishes safety and health standards with which employers and employees must comply.

1. _____

2. A formula measuring ____ compares the number of accident cases that have occurred with the total number of hours worked by employees during the same period.
3. The ____ Act requires all employees to comply with safety and health standards and rules applicable to their conduct.
4. A(n) ____ is any potentially dangerous condition, object, or practice in the workplace from which employees must be protected.
5. ____ refers to the procedure for determining how much money a disabled employee should receive as compensation for a job-related injury.
6. A formula that measures ____ compares the number of lost work days that have occurred with the total number of hours worked by all employees during the period.
7. A(n) ____ is an uncontrolled event that results in personal injury to an employee.
8. ____ is a measure that tells how often accidents have occurred.
9. Ignition of a substance with the heat generated by the rapid oxidation of its own constituents when exposed to air and with no other heat supplied is called ____.
10. To ____ a job for safety is to design the equipment, lay out the work, plan the job, and protect the individual, all with accident prevention in mind.

2. _____

3. _____

4. _____

5. _____

6. _____

7. _____

8. _____

9. _____

10. _____

Part B: TRUE-FALSE   By writing T or F in the space provided, indicate whether each statement is true or false.

Answers

1. Accidents are only rarely caused by people; generally, machine faults are the problem.
2. OSHA regulations require only employers to assume responsibility for preventing accidents.
3. When a company does not meet OSHA standards, a supervisor can be issued a citation for noncompliance.
4. Almost one-third of industrial accidents are caused by handling and lifting materials.
5. The National Safety Council maintains that accident prevention is dependent on engineering, education, and enforcement.
6. The effectiveness of applying the slogan "Safety first" comes from the supervisor.
7. An employee will probably not be influenced by the supervisor's wearing or using safety equipment.
8. Good housekeeping is one of the best fire prevention measures.
9. Examples of hazardous materials include coal dust, textile fibers, and vinyl chloride.
10. The term "low voltage" covers everything under 600 volts.

1. ____
2. ____
3. ____
4. ____
5. ____
6. ____
7. ____
8. ____
9. ____
10. ____

Part C: MULTIPLE CHOICE   Choose the response that best completes each statement. Write the letter of the response in the space provided.

Answers

1. The accident severity rate is based on the number of
   a. Accidents each year.
   b. Employees complaining about unsafe work conditions.
   c. Lost workdays caused by accidents.
   d. OSHA standards violated.

1. ____

2. Which of the following is not typically a major cause of accidents at work?
   a. A faulty protection device.
   b. Inadequate ventilation.
   c. Poorly defined federal regulations.
   d. Lack of safety training.

2. ____

3. Which of the following statements does OSHA require each employer to display on a poster?
   a. Safety is everyone's business.
   b. Safety first.
   c. The act further requires that employees comply with specific safety and health standards issued by the Department of Labor.
   d. Employees must create a workplace free of safety hazards and report all accidents.

3. ____

4. Each of the following is included in OSHA's General Environmental Controls section, except
   a. General sanitation.
   b. Extermination programs.
   c. Housekeeping.
   d. Safety training.

4. ____

5. Barb regularly wears loose-fitting clothing near the unguarded flywheel at her workstation. OSHA inspectors could do all of the following, except
   a. Require the employer to take disciplinary action against Barb.
   b. Cite Barb for not wearing required safe clothing.
   c. Cite the employer for not putting a guard on the machine.
   d. Require corrective action by the employer.

5. ____

6. Employees have the right, under the provisions of the Williams-Steiger Act, to do each of the following, except
   a. Request an inspection if they believe a violation of a standard exists.
   b. Refuse to work in an area they believe to be unsafe until an inspection is complete.
   c. Have regulations posted to inform them of protection afforded by the act.
   d. Have OSHA citations of the employer posted at work.

6. ____

7. Good supervisors know that
   a. Every safety rule may need to be broken occasionally.
   b. They are more influential than their employees in accident prevention.
   c. They should be specific about prevention techniques.
   d. All of the above.

7. ____

8. Scott's use of a protective eye shield is an example of using ____ to achieve job safety.
   a. Engineering.
   b. Education.
   c. Enforcement.
   d. Example.

8. ____

Chapter 21   **187**

9. The use of posters has been demonstrated to be least effective when they are
   a. Keyed to the work area's condition.
   b. Designed to "scare" people.
   c. Changed frequently.
   d. Used as part of an overall safety program.   9. ____

10. If hand tools are regularly used by employees, the supervisor should do all of the following, except
    a. Repair or throw away tools in bad shape.
    b. Assume employees know how to use all the tools.
    c. When using a tool from a new manufacturer, check the instruction manual.
    d. Make sure employees use the right tool for each job.   10. ____

Name _____ Date _____

22 The Supervisor's Role in Labor Relations

LEARNING OBJECTIVES

After studying this chapter, you should be able to

1. Discuss the supervisor's legal and operating responsibilities in labor-management relations.

2. Identify the significant provisions of the main labor-management relations laws.

3. Explain the collective bargaining process and its objectives.

4. Discuss supervisors' roles in implementing a labor agreement and their relationships with union representatives.

5. Describe a typical grievance procedure and discuss how a supervisor can contribute to its effectiveness.

Chapter Study Guide Outlines

Based on your study of the text chapter and/or your instructor's lesson presentation, complete the following outlines by supplying the correct answers for the numbered spaces. Some answers require more than one word to complete. Write the answers in the numbered answer column. Although you should rely principally on your recollection, you can use the textbook if you need help. Check your answers by referring to the keys at the back of this study guide.

▶ Supervision and Labor Unions

CONCEPT Supervisors are considered legal representatives of management in matters affecting labor union recognition and in the implementation of labor contracts that may result from it.

1. Legally, supervisors are the responsible agents of their companies. Employers are held __(1)__ for their supervisor's actions in dealing with employees or unions, as if they had taken the actions themselves.

Answers

1. _____

2. Employees join __(2)__ because
   a. Unions offer bargaining power and take risks through collective activity that many individuals cannot or do not wish to provide by acting alone.
   b. Membership, or at least payment of dues, is often __(3)__ .
   c. Membership provides both a real or perceived countervailing power from management's power to hire, promote, or fire at will.
3. If your company is unionized, work to get along with the union, but don't turn over to the union your interest in and __(4)__ to your employees.
4. Don't be hurt by the fact that employees have strong __(5)__ to their union as well as to their supervisor.

2. _____

3. _____

4. _____

5. _____

▶ 2 Labor-Management Law

CONCEPT Labor-management relations are governed by a large body of law: the most basic in the private sector is the National Labor Relations Act, which is administered by the National Labor Relations Board (NLRB).

1. The __(6)__ (Wagner Act) guarantees that employees may act as a group to bargain for wages, hours, and working conditions.
   a. The supervisor's job is more __(7)__ where unions exist, because the whole employee group position (according to the contract) must be taken into account when dealing with individual employee problems.
   b. Supervision has __(8)__ greatly since the right of employees to organize has been protected by law. Supervisors must avoid unfair labor practices during a union's organizing drive or representation election, including
      (1) Any actions that affect an employee's job or pay.
      (2) Arguments that lead to a dispute over a union question.
      (3) __(9)__ to a union member through a third party.
      (4) Interactions without advice from top management with any of the organizing union's officers.
2. The National Labor Relations Board is made up of five members appointed by the __(10)__ .
   a. The NLRB is responsible for
      (1) Administering the National Labor Relations Act, including determination of proper collective bargaining units.

6. _____

7. _____

8. _____

9. _____

10. _____

(2) Directing and supervising __(11)__ elections.

11. _____

(3) Preventing employers, employees, and unions from violating the act through unfair labor practices.

b. The NLRB is not a federal court and its rulings may be set aside by any __(12)__ .

12. _____

3. The Labor-Management Relations Act (Taft-Hartley Act, 1947) identified unfair labor practices and placed controls on union organizing activities, on the internal organization of unions, and on collective bargaining methods. Under this act

a. Unions and their agents are __(13)__ to

13. _____

(1) Attempt to force an employer to discharge a former member for reasons other than __(14)__ of dues or initiation fees.

14. _____

(2) Attempt to force an employer to pay for services that are not performed such as __(15)__ or make-work.

15. _____

(3) Restrain or coerce employees to join or not join a union.

(4) Require excessive or discriminatory union fees.

b. Individuals may take a __(16)__ directly to management if the issue and the settlement are not covered by the union contract and if a union representative is given the opportunity to attend.

16. _____

c. Other changes enacted by the Taft-Hartley Act include

(1) If either party wishes to terminate the contract, __(17)__ days' notice must be provided, during which time no strike, slowdown, or change in employment status or working conditions of any employee may occur.

17. _____

(2) Both labor and management may __(18)__ for damages caused by breach of contract.

18. _____

(3) Security guards are permitted to form their own bargaining unit but may not bargain collectively through a union associated with other employees.

(4) Both sides have freedom of speech except to utter threats of reprisal, or force, or promise of benefit.

(5) A __(19)__ shop—which requires that applicants be members of a union before they can be hired—is illegal.

19. _____

(6) A __(20)__ shop—which requires a new employee to join a union within a short period of time after employment—is legal. However, Taft-Hartley permits states to outlaw union shops, and 21 states have done so (right-to-work laws).

4. The Walsh-Healey Public Contract Act defines work days as 8 hours and the work week as 40 hours for companies with government contracts in excess of $10,000. __(21)__ pay is required for overtime.

5. The Fair Labor Standards Act regulates companies engaged in interstate commerce.

   a. Children over 14 and under 16 are restricted to non-manufacturing, nonmining jobs.

   b. Children between 16 and 18 are not permitted in hazardous jobs.

   c. The act establishes a minimum wage, which is periodically adjusted by Congress.

   d. Overtime must be paid for all hours after __(22)__ per week.

   e. Professional employees, who require advanced knowledge customarily required through prolonged instruction and study in a specialized field, are considered exempt from this legislation.

6. The labor-management reporting in the Disclosure Act of 1959 (Landrum-Griffith Act) is designed to prevent __(23)__, misuse of union funds, and so forth. It requires employers to report

   a. Payments to labor union officials, agents, or stewards (other than pay for work).

   b. Payment other than regular wage payments to employees or groups or committees for purposes of persuading other employees regarding a choice of a union or other union matters.

   c. Payment to __(24)__ on labor union matters.

20. _____

21. _____

22. _____

23. _____

24. _____

▶ 3 Union Representation and Collective Bargaining

CONCEPT   Supervisors are rarely involved directly in either the union organizing or the bargaining process, but their actions can deeply affect the results.

1. If __(25)__ of the employees request a recognition election, the NLRB will conduct one; if the union doesn't receive a majority of votes, the NLRB may not conduct another election for at least __(26)__ year.

25. _____

26. _____

2. During a recognition election campaign, a supervisor should
   a. Take instructions from the company.
   b. Represent the company in a positive light.
   c. Raise questions about employee relationships under union representation.
   d. Not promise __(27)__ for "no" votes.
   e. Not make threats about what will happen if the union gets in.
   f. Not pressure employees for their __(28)__ .
   g. Not spy on union activities.
   h. Not invite employees to his or her office to discuss the __(29)__ .

3. Collective __(30)__ between management and union establishes the wages, hours, and working conditions for union members.
   a. The final contract will depend on the reasonableness and desirability of demands, the ability to pay for the terms, the judgment concerning its worth, and the bargaining strength of union and management.
   b. __(31)__ of the contract occurs regularly during its life and requires skilled supervising, decision making, and administration of its terms and conditions.

27. _____

28. _____

29. _____

30. _____

31. _____

4▶ *Contract Administration*

CONCEPT   Supervisors are the pivotal implementers of labor contracts; they must deal constructively with union representatives without yielding their authority to manage.

1. A supervisor's actions could affect the entire company; the supervisor must strive to protect the interests and rights of __(32)__ .

32. _____

2. In addition to interference with an organizing drive, discussed earlier in this chapter, discrimination against an employee, because of union membership, is also considered an unfair labor practice according to the Wagner Act.

3. The supervisor's counterpart in the union is the __(33)__ , whose role is to represent the union in interpretation of contract provisions. Be cooperative, understanding, and patient, and keep shop stewards aware of what is going on. Try to resolve issues by seeking justice for employees within the contract.

33. _____

5 ▸ *Grievance Procedures*

CONCEPT   The grievance procedure provides a systematic, objective way of dealing with employee grievances.

1. Management and labor generally agree that a systematic method of handling __(34)__ is best.

34. _____

2. A grievance procedure is usually three to five steps long (see text Figure 22–1).

   a. Step 1: The supervisor discusses the complaint with the employee and union steward. Prompt action here can resolve as many as __(35)__ of all grievances.

35. _____

   b. Step 2: The superintendent and industrial relations manager discuss the complaint with the union grievance committee.

   c. Step 3: The site manager and labor relations manager discuss the complaint with the union grievance committee.

   d. Step 4: General company management discusses the complaint with the national union representative and union grievance committee.

   e. Step 5: The dispute is referred to an impartial umpire or __(36)__ for decision.

36. _____

3. A supervisor's grievance handling can be overturned because the supervisor acted on insufficient or incorrect facts, the company determines that its __(37)__ interpretation won't stand up to the union's position, or an arbitrator overrules the decision.

37. _____

4. Both unions and management prefer to solve their grievances without arbitration, but they prefer arbitration to __(38)__ and lockouts.

38. _____

COMMENTARY ON SELF-APPRAISAL FROM THE TEXT

This self-appraisal is, perhaps, the most difficult in the book. It requires interpretation and judgment on your part, and even the "panel of experts" can be faulted in theirs. This self-appraisal does, however, provide an example of the kinds of items that are the subject of collective bargaining and that often appear in key clauses of a labor contract. The degree of supervisor involvement, discretion, and action will vary widely from organization to organization. As such, this self-appraisal is especially useful for clarifying discretionary options for supervisors in a particular organizational setting.

1. Least likely. Noncontroversial.

2. Least likely. Noncontroversial.

3. Least likely. Noncontroversial.

4. Most likely. Procedures for evaluation and selection for promotions may be prescribed, but supervisors are usually deeply involved in the qualitative aspects of these decisions.

5. Most likely. Grievance procedures are "all supervisor" at the first step.

6. Least likely. Noncontroversial.

7. Most likely. Seniority practices may be prescribed, but they frequently require interpretation when applied to transfers (departmental seniority may prevail, for example) or layoffs (where craft or job seniority may be a factor). Supervisors would be consulted and their judgments considered in these instances.

8. Least likely. Noncontroversial.

9. Most likely. This could go either way, according to how it is viewed. If the contract stipulates call-in pay, it must be paid. But the supervisor becomes involved when a decision is required about whether to keep the employee on the job, even if there is no regular work available for the employee after he or she reported to work when called in.

10. Least likely. Noncontroversial.

11. Least likely. However, a supervisor's judgment may be requested if the situation is not clearly defined by contract procedures.

12. Least likely. Noncontroversial.

13. Least likely. Noncontroversial.

14. Most likely. It is almost impossible for a labor contract to spell out in advance every job assignment that may call for pay for hazardous or severely disagreeable work. Supervisors must often make a recommendation or render a decision.

15. Least likely. This, too, while spelled out in advance, may require supervisory discretion under unanticipated circumstances.

16. Most likely. Noncontroversial.

17. Least likely. Noncontroversial.

18. Least likely. Policy is set during bargaining; supervisors may become involved in deciding whether sickness was legitimate and whether reporting procedures were followed by the employee.

19. Least likely. Usually these decisions are made by the human resources staff.

20. Least likely. Noncontroversial.

SELF-CHECK OF YOUR PROGRESS

Part A: COMPLETION   An important term or phrase is needed to complete each of the following statements. Write the missing term in the space provided in the answer column.

1. If the union wins a(n) ____, management must then bargain collectively with employees through the union.
2. ____ occurs when authorized representatives of the employer and the employees bargain to establish wages, hours, and working conditions.
3. Interference and discrimination are two labor practices that most frequently involve ____.
4. The ____ places certain restrictions on unions or their agents relating to the internal organization of the union.
5. Individual states can pass ____ making the union shop illegal.
6. A ____ is a formalized system for employees to use in bringing their complaints to management.
7. Settlement of a labor dispute or employee grievance by an impartial third party is ____.
8. Actions taken by the union or management that interfere with employees' right to organize are ____.
9. The ____ directs and supervises recognition elections.
10. The written agreement that binds management and the union to certain conditions of pay and work for a given period of time is the ____.

Answers

1. _____

2. _____

3. _____

4. _____

5. _____

6. _____

7. _____

8. _____
9. _____

10. _____

Part B: TRUE-FALSE   By writing T or F in the space provided, indicate whether each statement is true or false.

Answers

1. According to the law, supervisors are the responsible agents of their companies.
2. It is perfectly all right for a supervisor to invite employees into the supervisor's office to discuss the union.
3. Collective bargaining can take place only after a union has won a representation election.
4. The Landrum-Griffith Act guarantees that employees may act in a group when bargaining for wages, hours, and working conditions.
5. Supervisors are frequently involved in bargaining sessions.
6. In a union shop, all employees must pay union dues, but they are not required to become union members.
7. The Labor Management Reporting and Disclosure Act of 1959 is aimed at preventing unethical collusion between a company and a union.
8. A supervisor's primary responsibility in labor matters is to keep disputes from accelerating.

1. ____

2. ____

3. ____

4. ____
5. ____

6. ____

7. ____

8. ____

9. The failure to collect all the facts is the most common cause of supervisors' being
overruled in the grievance procedure.   9. ____

10. Depending on the specific employment circumstances, a supervisor may be classified as either an exempt employee or a nonexempt employee.   10. ____

Part C: MULTIPLE CHOICE   Choose the response that best completes each
statement. Write the letter of the response in the space provided.

                                                                                         Answers

1. In the eyes of the law, employers
   a. Are responsible for any actions their supervisors take.
   b. Have the same legal relationship with their supervisors and general labor force.
   c. Can refuse to permit a union in their company.
   d. Can fire an employee for union involvement.   1. ____

2. The Wagner Act is also known as the
   a. Taft-Hartley Act.
   b. Right to Work Act.
   c. Fair Labor Standards Act.
   d. National Labor Relations Act.   2. ____

3. Once a union has been selected by employees through a representation election
   a. The union is authorized to negotiate a labor contract with management.
   b. Individual employees can no longer take up a grievance directly with manage-
      ment.
   c. The union may negotiate a closed shop.
   d. The union may sue for damages caused by breach of contract.   3. ____

4. Which of the following statements is true?
   a. The union shop requires applicants to be a member of the union before they can
      be hired.
   b. The closed shop forbids union membership.
   c. The union shop requires all employees, union member or not, to pay union
      dues.
   d. The open shop permits multiple unions to represent the same group of employees.   4. ____

5. The Landrum-Griffith Act of 1959
   a. Compels employers to report pay for work to labor union officials.
   b. Is designed to prevent collusion between employers and unions.
   c. Allows a union to refuse to disclose the disbursement of its funds.
   d. Prohibits payments to labor relations consultants.   5. ____

6. The NLRB
   a. Is appointed by the President of the United States.
   b. Supervises representation elections.
   c. Is empowered to interpret the National Labor Relations Act.
   d. All of the above.   6. ____

7. If a union is unsuccessful during a recognition election, it
   a. Can never represent those employees.
   b. May petition for another election after one year.
   c. Must wait two years before petitioning for another election.
   d. Can assist employees in negotiating their own employee contracts.   7. ____

8. Chico can help his employer by
   a. Promising employees rewards for not joining a union.
   b. Spying on union activities.
   c. Pressuring employees to commit to the company.
   d. Raising questions about employee relationships under union representation.   8. ___
9. A union steward has the authority to
   a. Officially interpret the contract.
   b. Examine all management records.
   c. Represent employees in disciplinary actions.
   d. All of the above.   9. ___
10. In a five-step grievance process, after the supervisor has discussed the complaint with the employee and union steward, the next step would typically be
   a. The superintendent and labor relations manager discuss the complaint with the union grievance committee.
   b. The supervisor informs the human resources department that a grievance has been filed.
   c. Arbitration.
   d. General company management discusses complaint with national union representative.   10. ___

Name _____   Date _____

Personal Development Portfolio:
Toward Mastery of Your Job

PORTFOLIO STUDY GUIDE OUTLINES

Based on your study of the text material and/or your instructor's lesson presentation, complete the following outlines by supplying the correct answers for the numbered spaces. Some answers require more than one word to complete. Write the answers in the numbered answer column. Although you should rely principally on your recollection, you can use the textbook if you need help. Check your answers by referring to the keys at the back of this study guide.

FILE 1   *Taking Charge of Your Career*

Answers

1. A __(1)__ program has four vital components:
   a. Candid self-assessment.
   b. Firm and realistic job goals.
   c. A concrete program for __(2)__.
   d. Motivation and commitment.
2. A __(3)__ maps the most logical and practical roadway to a position or series of positions that a person believes holds the most attractive occupational and personal rewards (see text Figure PDP–1).
3. Career plans must identify any personal __(4)__ in current performance and indicate the knowledge, skill, or experience needed to move from one step to another in the career path.
   a. Don't do too much too soon.
   b. Plan ahead one step at a time, making your plans in detail and planning realistically.
   c. Set __(5)__ to be reached (see text Figure PDP–2).
   d. Put goals and plans __(6)__ .
   e. Check your progress regularly.
4. __(7)__ refers to the informal associations built by or tapped by an individual to discover what is going on and what is opening up in an organization.
5. A __(8)__ is someone in a position of influence or authority who is interested in helping you and your career. This person is best used as an adviser.
6. The person with the better __(9)__ has an advantage over the person without it.
   a. If your attitude toward education is negative, change it.
   b. Identify your __(10)__ needs.

1. _____

2. _____

3. _____

4. _____

5. _____
6. _____

7. _____

8. _____

9. _____

10. _____

    Personal Development Portfolio   **199**

c. Take appropriate classes through correspondence at a local university or through adult education at a local high school.

d. Show an interest in your company's training and development program, including any management or __(11)__.

11. _____

e. Take advantage of outside help and guidance from either educational institutions or professional associations.

f. Try setting up a planned reading program, including a good newspaper, technical magazines, and books.

7. Keep your career goals compatible with your other __(12)__ in life.

12. _____

FILE 2 *Managing Job-Related Time*

1. Divide your time into two compartments:
   a. Time you can control.
   b. Time you can't control.

2. __(13)__ is guided by two rules:

13. _____

   a. Systematize and prioritize the management of your controllable time.
   b. Minimize the amount of __(14)__ time.

14. _____

3. Seven guidelines to manage your time better are
   a. Make up your mind fast: __(15)__ of the problems you face aren't worth more than a few minutes of your time.

15. _____

   b. Be __(16)__ about dates.

16. _____

   c. Control the telephone.
   d. Write down reminders.
   e. Limit chitchat.
   f. Set up a time budget, placing your time allotments in four categories (see text Figure PDP–3):
      (1) __(17)__ work.

17. _____

      (2) Regular job duties.
      (3) Special assignments.
      (4) __(18)__ work.

18. _____

   g. Begin each workday with a plan.

4. ABC analysis predicts that 80 percent of your time will be spent on __(19)__ of your problems.

19. _____

   a. Each task is labeled A, vital; B, not quite as important; or C, not important (most problems will appear here).
   b. Spend your time on the __(20)__ first.

20. _____

5. In judging a problem's importance, ask
   a. Where did it come from?
   b. What is its potential for trouble?
   c. Is it aimed at results rather than activity?
   d. How quickly can it be disposed of?

FILE 3 *Coping With Stress*

1. People who don't show the signs of stress, frustration, and/or pressure on their mind, nerves, or body
   a. Have learned their stress __(21)__ .
   b. Have kept their stress load within them.
2. You "manage" stress by finding ways to relieve it, redistribute it, or remove it.
3. Stress at work comes from
   a. The work environment.
   b. Your inner self.
   c. __(22)__ relationships.
4. The goal of stress management is to eliminate persistent but __(23)__ stress, including
   a. __(24)__ about the results for which you are held responsible—seek clarity in performance expectations.
   b. __(25)__ for the job at hand—be sure you have the necessary labor, equipment, materials, and supplies.
   c. Conflicting demands and instructions—make the results of conflicts clear to all parties.
5. Stress outside of work is often more powerful and less manageable; therefore, you must
   a. Alter or change the conditions of your personal environment to reduce stress, if you can.
   b. Be realistic about your personal ambitions and capabilities.
   c. Identify the necessary interpersonal transactions where your performance is unsatisfactory and improve it.
6. Lessen the impact of stress on your life:
   a. Understand your __(26)__ and live within them.
   b. __(27)__ , if necessary, before you break yourself.
   c. Get more genuine __(28)__ .
   d. Select and pursue at least one __(29)__ .
   e. Take time to look at the world around you.

21. _____

22. _____

23. _____
24. _____

25. _____

26. _____
27. _____
28. _____
29. _____

1. To gain personal acceptance in an organization
   a. Demonstrate your job __(30)__ .
   b. Become an integral part of the information network
      by knowing
      (1) The extent of unique information in the organi-
          zation.
      (2) How to __(31)__ to it.
      (3) How to contribute to it.
      (4) How to __(32)__ in your operation.
   c. Go with the flow of the organization.
   d. Build a personal support system.
      (1) Develop a good relationship with a __(33)__ in
          the department that precedes and follows yours
          in the production line.
      (2) Establish contacts with key staff departments.
2. Attitudes and actions you should avoid include
   a. Being unwilling to pull your weight.
   b. Holding a __(34)__ attitude toward your peers.
   c. Being characterized as a __(35)__ person who resists
      change.
   d. Taking all the credit.
3. Your good works will go unnoticed unless you make a
   conscious effort to display them.
   a. Exhibit your leadership and initiative.
   b. Look for, or accept, __(36)__ responsibilities.
4. There are several tactics you should consider when asking for a raise:
   a. Come right out and ask for it—be certain your per-
      formance warrants it, and be prepared with the
      facts.
   b. Pick a __(37)__.
      (1) Make it reasonable in light of
          (a) Your performance.
          (b) What others are being paid.
      (2) Don't set it too low, and be prepared to
          __(38)__ .
   c. Stress the value of your contributions.
      (1) Document your productivity, dependability,
          management-mindedness, and initiative.
      (2) Avoid saying you need the money.
   d. Wait and see.

30. _____

31. _____

32. _____

33. _____

34. _____

35. _____

36. _____

37. _____

38. _____

COMMENTARY ON THE FOUR SELF-ASSESSMENT EXERCISES FROM THE TEXT

Table PDP–1: PERSONAL EFFECTIVENESS INVENTORY   The 11 skills or competencies listed in the exercise are representative of those usually cited as necessary for supervisory development and advancement. They do not represent an exhaustive list, however. Other lists contain such qualities and competencies as basic job knowledge or technical know-how, conceptualization, rationality, self-control, objectivity, energy and stamina, self-confidence, motivational skills, training and coaching skills, integrity and trustworthiness, emotional resilience, and self-knowledge.

Table PDP–2: TIME MANAGEMENT SURVEY   The 10 items in the survey are simply a sampling of practices that are generally believed to lead to sound time management and control. Be cautioned that your scores are based on a self-administered survey. Some people may have "beaten" the survey by anticipating that high numbers were desirable and low numbers were to be avoided. The intention of the survey is to provide standards of practice against which you can judge your own habits. Hence, the survey is a learning exercise, not necessarily a measuring instrument.

Table PDP–3: STRESS INDICATOR BAROMETER   All the items in the exercise represent either (1) signs of maladjustment to stress or (2) susceptibility to stress. Hence, the exercise represents a logical, but not necessarily a scientific, mixture of items. Taken together, they are an indication of the presence of heavy stress or of attitudes and perceptions that lead to stressful situations. Scoring is provided simply to challenge your awareness and to stimulate learning. Scores should not be interpreted as having either psychological or medical authority. Items 4, 6, and 18 are believed to be indicative of Type A individuals, who tend to induce stress in themselves and in the work situations in which they are engaged.

Table PDP–4: ORGANIZATIONAL ACCEPTANCE RATING SHEET   All the items in this exercise are reflected in the text material of File 4. As with the time management survey, you may "beat" the rating by anticipating which numbers are favorable and which are unfavorable. Here again, the intention of the exercise is to provide you with an awareness of conditions that represent an acceptance of a supervisor by the organization and by her or his boss. Thus, it is a learning exercise, not a measuring instrument.

SELF-CHECK OF YOUR PROGRESS

Part A: COMPLETION   An important term or phrase is needed to complete each of the following statements. Write the missing term in the space provided in the answer column.

Answers

1. A supervisor's ____ can be demonstrated by the presence of well-motivated employees who are under control.

1. _____

2. A(n) ____ is a group of people working together toward common goals.

2. _____

3. Supervisors can demonstrate their ____ by volunteering, with discrimination, to do extra work.

3. _____

4. Pressure on a person's physical, mental, or nervous system is known as ____ .

4. _____

5. A supervisor can work around distractions if he or she uses a(n) ____.
6. ____ items on the daily schedule can help a supervisor get important projects out of the way.
7. ____ predicts that 80 percent of a supervisor's time will be spent on 20 percent of the problems.
8. Stress comes from both work and ____ environments.
9. Concentrate your attention on the ____ problems and let the trivial many wait their turn.
10. Stress in its exaggerated state is often called ____.

5. _____
6. _____
7. _____
8. _____
9. _____
10. _____

Part B: TRUE-FALSE   By writing T or F in the space provided, indicate whether each statement is true or false.

Answers

1. The first step in a career path calls for a supervisor to move to the next higher position in the organization.

1. ____

2. In making plans for self-improvement or career development, plan ahead one step at a time.

2. ____

3. A mentor is best used in an advisory capacity.

3. ____

4. Career goals are often in conflict with family plans.

4. ____

5. Maturity enables individuals to make objective assessments of their strengths and weaknesses.

5. ____

6. It is unnecessary for a supervisor to become involved in a company's information network.

6. ____

7. To be successful, any organization must be a cooperative effort.

7. ____

8. A line supervisor can work without the cooperation of key staff departments and still be successful.

8. ____

9. When asking for a raise, a supervisor should be sure not to request too low a figure.

9. ____

10. A supervisor should systematize and prioritize the management of uncontrollable time.

10. ____

Part C: MULTIPLE CHOICE   Choose the response that best completes each statement. Write the letter of the response in the space provided.

Answers

1. Career development is based partly on
   a. Forcing others out of key positions.
   b. Firm and realistic goals.
   c. Motivation and commitment.
   d. Both b and c.

1. ____

2. A mentor is a person who
   a. Supervises the supervisors.
   b. Helps supervisors develop career goals.
   c. Has authority and is interested in a person's career development.
   d. Is the most important part of a network.

2. ____

3. Networking is
   a. A formal communication system that goes across departments.
   b. A way of handling human problems by changing behavior.
   c. Planning career development by using a mentor.
   d. An informal way for a person to keep up with what's going on in an organization.

3. ____

4. Management development is a method
   a. For managers to define their career goals.
   b. By which a company recognizes management potential among supervisors.
   c. For the systematic training and appraisal of management.
   d. For individuals to increase the scope of their positions.   4. ____
5. Individuals may improve on their education by
   a. Doing outside reading.
   b. Attending adult education classes.
   c. Enrolling in for-credit college courses.
   d. All of the above.   5. ____
6. Maria will manage her time better if she does each of the following, except
   a. Make up her mind fast.
   b. Be flexible about due dates.
   c. Control the telephone.
   d. None of the above.   6. ____
7. ABC analysis helps the supervisor understand
   a. The value of handling problems in the order they come in.
   b. That routine work is always the most important.
   c. That creative work happens most often at night.
   d. That the best use of time is to concentrate on the class A vital problems.   7. ____
8. Work-related stress comes from
   a. The work environment.
   b. Your inner self.
   c. Interpersonal relationships.
   d. All of the above.   8. ____
9. When Jackie asks questions like "How good?" and "How soon?" she is trying to avoid stress resulting from
   a. Ambiguity about results she will be held accountable for.
   b. Inadequate resources to do the job.
   c. Conflicting demands and instructions.
   d. Her own limitations.   9. ____
10. Which of the following ideas is recommended when asking your boss for a raise?
   a. Let the boss propose a salary increase and react to it.
   b. Let the boss bring up the subject.
   c. Stress the value of your contribution.
   d. Don't negotiate; stick to your recommendation.   10. ____

Keys to the Study Guide

CHAPTER 1

KEY TO CHAPTER 1 STUDY GUIDE OUTLINES

1. Management
2. Executives
3. Middle managers
4. Supervisors
5. Fair Labor Standards Act
6. less than 20 percent
7. overtime
8. Taft-Hartley Act
9. union of production or clerical workers
10. union of supervisors
11. college or technical school
12. another company
13. organizational skills
14. employees
15. himself or herself
16. keystones
17. self-assurance
18. management
19. staff specialists
20. objective relation ships
21. Keeping operating costs in line
22. Energy, power, and utilities
23. Human resources
24. Money
25. Costs and budget control
26. Planning
27. Organizing
28. Staffing
29. Activating
30. Controlling
31. Administrative skills
32. managerial
33. human relations
34. employee-centered
35. 50 to 80

SELF-CHECK OF YOUR PROGRESS
Part A: COMPLETION

1. 20
2. supervising
3. organizational goals
4. resources
5. Conservation
6. results
7. technical
8. administrative
9. executive
10. process

Part B: TRUE-FALSE

1. F   3. T   5. F   7. F   9. T
2. F   4. T   6. T   8. F   10. T

Part C: MULTIPLE CHOICE

1. c   3. b   5. a   7. b   9. d
2. c   4. d   6. b   8. c   10. b

CHAPTER 2

KEY TO CHAPTER 2 STUDY GUIDE OUTLINES

1. inside
2. shortest
3. Technology
4. Legal restrictions
5. organizational goals
6. other supervisors
7. recorded information
8. Internationalization
9. women
10. Money
11. satisfaction
12. bureaucracy
13. degree of conformity
14. responsible
15. behind
16. written records
17. 80 to 90
18. Older
19. younger
20. five
21. too easy
22. entitlements
23. flexible
24. motivation
25. Expectations
26. information
27. productivity
28. decision making
29. "bottom-upward"
30. flexible

SELF-CHECK OF YOUR PROGRESS
Part A: COMPLETION

1. Work
2. money (or equivalent term)
3. bureaucracy
4. higher
5. downsizing
6. facilitating
7. boredom
8. the supervisor
9. entitlements
10. feedback

Part B: TRUE-FALSE

1. F   3. F   5. F   7. F   9. F
2. T   4. F   6. F   8. T   10. T

Part C: MULTIPLE CHOICE

1. a   3. c   5. d   7. d   9. a
2. b   4. c   6. a   8. c   10. d

CHAPTER 3

KEY TO CHAPTER 3 STUDY GUIDE OUTLINES

1. thinking and acting
2. systematic
3. Planning
4. Organizing
5. Staffing
6. Activating
7. Controlling
8. resources
9. end result
10. service
11. valuable
12. division of work
13. unity of command
14. unity of direction
15. second
16. chain of command
17. initiative
18. systematic management
19. human relations
20. technical
21. Contingency
22. situation
23. Japanese manage-ment
24. interrelated
25. dependent
26. situational

SELF-CHECK OF YOUR PROGRESS
Part A: COMPLETION

1. outputs
2. management process
3. resources
4. quantitative
5. contingency
6. direction
7. command
8. chain of command
9. division of work
10. system

Part B: TRUE-FALSE

I. T	3. F	5. F	7. F	9. T
2. T	4. T	6. T	8. F	10. F

Part C: MULTIPLE CHOICE

1. c	3. d	5. b	7. c	9. c
2. a	4. b	6. a	8. d	10. b

CHAPTER 4

KEY TO CHAPTER 4 STUDY GUIDE OUTLINES

1. machinery
2. human resources
3. short-range
4. long-range
5. policies
6. Schedules
7. strengths and weaknesses
8. attainable
9. priority order
10. output
11. terms or numbers
12. plan
13. Explain
14. Standing
15. Single-use
16. 100 percent
17. stress and fatigue
18. production-control
19. bottlenecks
20. complex or one-of-a-kind
21. organizational
22. high-level
23. Supervisors
24. not
25. policy

SELF-CHECK OF YOUR PROGRESS
Part A: COMPLETION

1. procedures
2. objectives
3. higher-level managers
4. single-use
5. Long-range
6. PERT
7. work-distribution
8. regulations
9. production-control chart
10. Scheduling

Part B: TRUE-FALSE

1. F	3. T	5. T	7. F	9. F
2. F	4. F	6. T	8. T	10. T

Part C: MULTIPLE CHOICE

1. c	3. b	5. c	7. a	9. a
2. a	4. c	6. d	8. c	10. d

CHAPTER 5

KEY TO CHAPTER 5 STUDY GUIDE OUTLINES

1. problem
2. action
3. actual
4. 80
5. minor
6. Current
7. advance
8. deviation
9. performance
10. removing
11. choice
12. information
13. causes
14. most likely
15. solutions
16. plan of action
17. intuition
18. uncertainty
19. decision tree
20. alternative solution
21. Cost-benefit analysis
22. public
23. profit
24. logic and intuition
25. Programmed
26. all
27. need
28. act
29. commitment
30. time
31. greatest gain or loss
32. perspective
33. fallback
34. obtaining
35. value
36. management infor-mation system
37. accounting
38. computer-based
39. Information
40. end users
41. inputs
42. Primary data
43. Secondary data
44. job dissatisfaction
45. monotonous
46. irritations
47. normal

SELF-CHECK OF YOUR PROGRESS
Part A: COMPLETION

1. change
2. intuition
3. systematic
4. action
5. decision tree
6. ABC analysis
7. programmed
8. input source
9. primary
10. MIS

Part B: TRUE-FALSE

Part B: TRUE-FALSE

1. T	3. T	5. F	7. F	9. F
2. T	4. T	6. T	8. F	10. T

Part C: MULTIPLE CHOICE

I. d	3. c	5. d	7. b	9. c
2. a	4. c	6. a	8. d	10. a

CHAPTER 6

KEY TO CHAPTER 6 STUDY GUIDE OUTLINES

1. goals	16. constantly
2. work relationships	17. Informal
3. human resources	18. Responsibilities
4. one person	19. Authority
5. responsibilities	20. Interpersonal skills
6. simple	21. Limited authority
7. line	22. functional authority
8. advice or service duties	23. most important
9. done (doers)	24. Confidential
10. staff	25. appraisal
11. product	26. relative importance
12. Geographic	27. Undercontrolling
13. project manager	28. chain of command
14. many levels	29. confidences
15. Span of control	30. too long

SELF-CHECK OF YOUR PROGRESS
Part A: COMPLETION

1. division of labor	6. relationships
2. human resources	7. matrix
3. advisers	8. authority
4. delegation	9. span of control
5. chain of command	10. customer-oriented

Part B: TRUE-FALSE

1. T	3. T	5. T	7. T	9. F
2. F	4. F	6. F	8. F	10. T

Part C: MULTIPLE CHOICE

1. a	3. a	5. d	7. b	9. c
2. c	4. a	6. a	8. b	10. d

CHAPTER 7

KEY TO CHAPTER 7 STUDY GUIDE OUTLINE

1. staffing	32. not
2. resource	33. release
3. performance	34. Personal
4. costly	35. overview
5. good care	36. unfavorable
6. improve	37. physical demands
7. working conditions	38. worksite and job
8. produce	location
9. Calculate	39. advancement
10. indirect employees	40. rapport
11. temporary	41. point-blank questions
12. workload	42. how and when
13. Overstaffing	43. Open-ended
14. Understaffing	questions
15. jobs	44. sexual preference
16. Forecasting	45. citizenship
17. Recruiting	46. no guarantees
18. screening	47. two or more sources
19. candidates	48. Desirable
20. Hiring	49. Work motivation
21. Application forms	50. "self-fulfilling
22. interviews	prophecy"
23. references	51. existing employees
24. tests	52. reputation
25. teamwork	53. ineffective
26. validated	54. rate of turnover
27. legal requirements	55. lower
28. Reliability	56. morale
29. after	57. selection and
30. perform	placement
31. reasonable accom-	58. Absenteeism
modation	59. supervision

SELF-CHECK OF YOUR PROGRESS
Part A: COMPLETION

1. absenteeism rate	6. illegal
2. forecasting	7. Reliability
3. Aptitude	8. application blank
4. turnover	9. realistic job preview
5. Validity	10. interview

Part B: TRUE-FALSE

1. T	3. T	5. F	7. F	9. T
2. T	4. T	6. F	8. F	10. T

Part C: MULTIPLE CHOICE

1. c	3. a	5. c	7. d	9. d
2. b	4. c	6. c	8. d	10. d

CHAPTER 8

KEY TO CHAPTER 8 STUDY GUIDE

1. company training
2. high school
3. 10 percent
4. productivity
5. improved
6. requires
7. skill
8. instruction
9. learning
10. correspondence
11. adequate
12. supervisor
13. formally
14. scrap or rework
15. overtime
16. employee selection
17. job-related
18. needs
19. who
20. what
21. solution
22. skill tests
23. "skills inventory"
24. do
25. Plan
26. teacher and coach
27. responsibilities
28. solve problems
29. improvement
30. supportive
31. open-ended
32. constructive
33. day
34. invested
35. worker
36. self-directed
37. evaluations
38. standardized
39. hired
40. Orientation
41. safety rules
42. department
43. coworkers
44. small doses
45. Skill
46. dividing
47. key point
48. easiest
49. few
50. advancement
51. knowledge-based or skill-based
52. shift
53. interested
54. training
55. minds
56. why
57. different
58. speed
59. quickly
60. Older
61. Selection
62. skill development
63. one time
64. Apprentice training
65. years
66. organization
67. Visual aids
68. speeds
69. job aid
70. forgetting
71. infrequently
72. all
73. actively
74. Self-paced method
75. Direct
76. Indirect
77. promotion
78. objectives
79. performance
80. Praising
81. specific
82. demonstrations
83. buddy

SELF-CHECK YOUR PROGRESS
Part A: COMPLETION

1. induction training
2. coaching
3. knowledge
4. key point
5. self-directed learning
6. Skill
7. Teachable moments
8. programmed instruction
9. job breakdown
10. Job aids

Part B: TRUE-FALSE

1. F	3. T	5. F	7. T	9. T
2. T	4 T	6. T	8. T	10. T

Part C: MULTIPLE CHOICE

1. b	3. d	5. b	7. d	9. c
2. a	4. b	6. b	8. d	10. c

CHAPTER 9

KEY TO CHAPTER 9 STUDY GUIDE

1. understand
2. motivate
3. personality
4. predict
5. reasons
6. five
7. hierarchy
8. survival
9. esteem
10. self-actualization
11. satisfied
12. fulfill
13. supervisor
14. employees
15. appreciated
16. mind and skills
17. dissatisfaction
18. motivating
19. on the job
20. parent organization
21. attaining goals
22. control
23. moderate
24. feedback
25. task orientation
26. Power
27. influence
28. whether or not
29. assert
30. friendly
31. cooperation
32. management
33. rewarded
34. satisfactory
35. fairness
36. rewards
37. inequity
38. contributions
39. process-centered
40. Process-flow
41. Work space layout
42. redesigned
43. physiological
44. unnecessary
45. Empowerment
46. resolve
47. control
48. freedom
49. Job enlargement
50. specialists
51. turnover
52. cooperation

SELF-CHECK YOUR PROGRESS
Part A: COMPLETION

1. needs
2. social
3. self-actualization
4. satisfied
5. esteem
6. maintenance (hygiene) factors
7. Equity
8. job redesign
9. power
10. achievement

Part B: TRUE-FALSE

1. F	3. F	5. F	7. F	9. T
2. F	4 T	6. T	8. F	10. F

Part C: MULTIPLE CHOICE

| 1. a | 3. c | 5. a | 7. d | 9. d |
| 2. c | 4. c | 6. d | 8. b | 10. a |

CHAPTER 10

KEY TO CHAPTER 10 STUDY GUIDE OUTLINES

1. Leadership
2. reasonable
3. productivity
4. conservation of resources
5. commitment
6. skills
7. responsibility
8. stronger
9. Charisma
10. moderate
11. energy
12. persuasion
13. Motivation
14. needs
15. motivate
16. understanding
17. satisfaction
18. leadership
19. Theory X
20. Dislike
21. coerced
22. responsibility
23. Theory Y
24. natural
25. self-control
26. committed
27. rewards
28. achievement
29. responsibility
30. problem-solving
31. realized
32. leadership
33. minor
34. total approach
35. directive style
36. short-run results
37. absenteeism and turnover
38. decision
39. "consensus"
40. less effective
41. participative
42. empower
43. implement
44. committed
45. immediately
46. control
47. time
48. benefits
49. interesting
50. employees
51. Suggestion
52. total quality management
53. ownership
54. Managerial Grid©
55. Situational
56. contingency
57. leader–member
58. structure
59. power
60. participative
61. circumstances
62. life-cycle
63. competence
64. commitment
65. job experiences
66. Clarifying
67. directive
68. supportive
69. delegating
70. crisis
71. follower
72. capabilities
73. self-leadership
74. win–win
75. operation
76. Substitutes
77. cohesive
78. positive
79. independence
80. rigid
81. popular
82. please
83. responsible
84. equitable

Part A: COMPLETION

1. contingency
2. leadership
3. need
4. democratic leadership
5. continuum leadership
6. participative
7. persuasion
8. Managerial Grid©
9. Y
10. superleaders

Part B: TRUE-FALSE

| 1. F | 3. F | 5. F | 7. T | 9. T |
| 2. T | 4 T | 6. F | 8. T | 10. T |

Part C: MULTIPLE CHOICE

| 1. b | 3. c | 5. a | 7. a | 9. c |
| 2. b | 4. b | 6. d | 8. a | 10. d |

CHAPTER 11

KEY TO CHAPTER 11 STUDY GUIDE

1. information
2. Repeat
3. linking pin
4. leadership
5. sensitive
6. Three-dimensional
7. horizontally
8. 360-degree feedback
9. specific task
10. Spoken
11. Informal talks
12. appointments
13. Telephone calls
14. Written
15. Reports
16. mass meetings
17. analyze
18. grapevine
19. louder
20. eye contact
21. verbal
22. interrupt
23. ideas
24. informed
25. unprepared
26. personal
27. sexual
28. performance
29. properly
30. specific
31. confidence
32. problem
33. person
34. objects
35. requests
36. power
37. feedback
38. orders
39. conflicting
40. authority

SELF-CHECK OF YOUR PROGRESS
Part A: COMPLETION

1. communication process
2. three-dimensional
3. body language
4. feedback
5. informal talk
6. planned conference
7. Communication media
8. Noise
9. grapevine
10. Active listening

Part B: True-False

1. T	3. T	5. T	7. T	9. F
2. T	4. T	6. F	8. T	10. F

Part C: MULTIPLE CHOICE

1. d	3. a	5. c	7. d	9. c
2. b	4. d	6. a	8. b	10. c

CHAPTER 12

KEY TO CHAPTER 12 STUDY GUIDE

1. good behavior	21. improvement
2. career	22. facts
3. twice	23. blame
4. company policies	24. you
5. job-pricing	25. private
6. purpose	26. Sandwich
7. separate	27. Document
8. Legal responsibilities	28. high ratings
9. Forced-choice	29. rewarding
10. Subjective	30. Appraise
11. Double check	31. performance
12. high	32. mature
13. critical incidents	33. Equal
14. halo effect	34. discrimination
15. communicated	35. Accommodation
16. Behaviorally anchored rating scale	36. job
	37. written
17. activity	38. improvement
18. court	39. Comparable worth
19. management by objectives	40. capabilities
	41. work group
20. accomplishments	42. operating

SELF-CHECK ON YOUR PROGRESS
Part A: COMPLETION

1. appraisal	6. Compensation
2. critical incident	7. forced-choice
3. saving face	8. objective
4. Job evaluation	9. MBO
5. performance appraisal	10. Comparable worth

Part B: TRUE-FALSE

1. F	3. T	5. T	7. T	9. T
2. F	4. F	6. T	8. F	10. T

Part C: MULTIPLE CHOICE

1. c	3. b	5. a	7. c	9. a
2. d	4. c	6. d	8. b	10. d

CHAPTER 13

KEY TO CHAPTER 13 STUDY GUIDE

1. quality	30. silence
2. performance	31. open-ended
3. temporary	32. interview
4. troubled	33. appreciation
5. emotionally disturbed	34. private
6. personal assistance	35. professional
7. Workaholics	36. report
8. balance	37. psychiatrist
9. expensive	38. psychologist
10. minor	39. authority
11. Hiring	40. illnesses
12. acceptable	41. well
13. professional	42. rules
14. run away	43. penalties
15. dissatisfied	44. Job satisfaction
16. insubordinate	45. unpleasant
17. stress	46. immediate
18. Psychological	47. chronically
19. Psychosocial	48. legal
20. empathetic	49. substance-abuse
21. fire	50. throughout
22. task-oriented	51. Partial
23. recognize	52. confronting
24. responsible	53. explanation
25. solve	54. alcoholic
26. personal	55. responsibility
27. catharsis	56. constructive coercion
28. patiently	57. Detection
29. argue	58. transitional

SELF-CHECK YOUR PROGRESS
Part A: COMPLETION

1. neurosis	6. psychosis
2. adjustment	7. stress
3. catharsis	8. alcoholism
4. Employee counseling	9. Drug addiction
5. Hostility	10. withdrawal

Part B: TRUE-FALSE

1. F	3. F	5. F	7. F	9. F
2. T	4. F	6. T	8. T	10. T

Part C: MULTIPLE CHOICE

1. b	3. c	5. d	7. c	9. c
2. d	4. a	6. d	8. b	10. d

CHAPTER 14

KEY TO CHAPTER 14 STUDY GUIDE

1. interdependence
2. Formal
3. Informal
4. tightest
5. emerge
6. helpful
7. disapproved
8. standards
9. cut off
10. personal sacrifices
11. limitations
12. risk taking
13. conflict
14. unique perspectives
15. solving problems
16. coach
17. veto power
18. actively involved
19. committed
20. group
21. minimum interference
22. Organizational development
23. overcontrolled
24. intervention
25. Encounter
26. Team building
27. leader
28. inevitable
29. cross purposes
30. work itself
31. mistrust
32. Competition
33. bargain
34. outcomes
35. Transactional analysis
36. dependence
37. parental
38. mature
39. stroking
40. advantage
41. want
42. intelligent
43. expense
44. lend a hand
45. cooperation breeds cooperation
46. critical feedback
47. trust them

SELF-CHECK YOUR PROGRESS
Part A: COMPLETION

1. Organizational development
2. informal work groups
3. formal work group
4. group norms or norms
5. competition
6. conflict
7. transactional analysis
8. Morale
9. not okay
10. stroking

Part B: TRUE-FALSE

1. T	3. F	5. T	7. T	9. F
2. T	4. F	6. F	8. T	10. F

Part C: MULTIPLE CHOICE

1. b	3. c	5. d	7. a	9. c
2. a	4. b	6. b	8. b	10. a

CHAPTER 15

KEY TO CHAPTER 15 STUDY GUIDE

1. production goals
2. judgmental
3. problem-solving or decision-making
4. Controls
5. machine
6. organizational
7. numerically
8. standard
9. systematic analysis
10. performance standards
11. measure
12. corrective
13. deviation
14. key places
15. Concurrent
16. automatic
17. resentment
18. Output
19. inspections
20. Statistical quality control
21. Time
22. Material
23. Cost
24. Management by exception
25. corrective action
26. numbers
27. improvement
28. threats
29. self-control
30. managers
31. self-control

SELF-CHECK YOUR PROGRESS
Part A: COMPLETION

1. judgmental
2. problem solving
3. Control
4. standards
5. tolerance
6. taking corrective action
7. quality control
8. self-control
9. Preventive
10. automatic

Part B: TRUE-FALSE

1. F	3. F	5. F	7. F	9. F
2. F	4. T	6. T	8. T	10. T

Part C: MULTIPLE CHOICE

1. d	3. c	5. d	7. c	9. a
2. b	4. a	6. a	8. d	10. c

CHAPTER 16

KEY TO CHAPTER 16 STUDY GUIDE

1. cost control
2. up-to-date
3. Unit
4. Standard
5. Budgeted
6. allowable
7. output
8. cost-variance
9. fixed
10. Cost reduction
11. central operations
12. "action-now"
13. returns
14. Most obvious
15. Worst first
16. payback
17. employees
18. Cost reduction committees
19. waste
20. wisely
21. space
22. quickly
23. competition
24. security
25. managers
26. prenegotiation
27. weakening
28. international competition
29. interests
30. goals
31. cost improvement

SELF-CHECK OF YOUR PROGRESS
Part A: COMPLETION

1. standards
2. cost-variance report
3. fixed
4. Unit
5. budget
6. "belt tightening"
7. cost reduction
8. unit
9. Direct
10. Indirect

Part B: TRUE-FALSE

1. F	3. F	5. T	7. F	9. F
2. T	4. T	6. T	8. T	10. T

Part C: MULTIPLE CHOICE

1. c	3. b	5. d	7. c	9. c
2. a	4. a	6. d	8. b	10. c

CHAPTER 17

KEY TO CHAPTER 17 STUDY GUIDE

1. performance management
2. discipline
3. punitive
4. authority or power
5. absenteeism
6. sexual harassment
7. identify
8. decide
9. jury
10. development
11. logic
12. administer
13. personal
14. equal treatment
15. Positive
16. Progressive
17. immediacy
18. consistency
19. supervisors
20. solve
21. evaluate
22. future
23. Behavior modification
24. view
25. solution
26. plan
27. warning
28. Facts
29. constructive
30. written
31. Suspension
32. work record
33. privacy
34. argumentative
35. benefits
36. department
37. "just cause"
38. performance
39. penalties
40. displayed
41. imposed
42. Due process
43. customers
44. unsatisfactory
45. appraisal

SELF-CHECK OF YOUR PROGRESS
Part A: COMPLETION

1. Behavior modification
2. discipline
3. equal treatment
4. Progressive
5. advance warning
6. consistency
7. facts
8. Due process
9. suspension
10. warning

Part B: TRUE-FALSE

1. T	3. F	5. F	7. T	9. T
2. T	4. T	6. T	8. T	10. F

Part C: MULTIPLE CHOICE

1. b	3. c	5. a	7. c	9. b
2. c	4. a	6. c	8. a	10. b

CHAPTER 18

KEY TO CHAPTER 18 STUDY GUIDE

1. output
2. inputs
3. percentage
4. productivity
5. increase
6. decrease
7. productivity
8. human
9. mechanization
10. knowledge
11. pay
12. improvement
13. face-to-face
14. satisfaction
15. quality circle
16. Work measurement
17. Time
18. sampling
19. instant
20. reliable
21. wages
22. lower cost
23. quality
24. systems engineering
25. when
26. necessary
27. value
28. Transportation
29. Storage
30. makeready
31. eliminating
32. simple
33. comfortable
34. shrinking
35. Reengineering
36. high-tech
37. forgiving
38. counsel
39. "use and esteem"
40. overview
41. free association
42. concentrate
43. Preserve
44. flowing
45. action
46. criticize

SELF-CHECK OF YOUR PROGRESS
Part A: COMPLETION

1. Productivity
2. human
3. satisfaction
4. Work measurement
5. Work sampling
6. motion economy
7. value analysis
8. Reengineering
9. Work simplification
10. standard

Part B: TRUE-FALSE

1. F
2. T
3. T
4. F
5. F
6. T
7. T
8. T
9. T
10. F

Part C: MULTIPLE CHOICE

1. c
2. a
3. b
4. b
5. d
6. c
7. b
8. c
9. d
10. c

CHAPTER 19

KEY TO CHAPTER 19 STUDY GUIDE

1. Total quality management
2. negative
3. conformity
4. Nondestructive
5. billions
6. 2 to 10 percent
7. warranties
8. 3
9. shared
10. activity
11. judge
12. above
13. into
14. personal
15. irregular
16. immediately
17. first
18. communication
19. tools
20. numbers
21. cause
22. Sampling
23. without
24. rejecting
25. member
26. commitment
27. immediately
28. involved
29. voluntary
30. labor relations
31. simple
32. labor union
33. investigating
34. negotiate
35. contacts
36. customer
37. Internal

SELF-CHECK OF YOUR PROGRESS
Part A: COMPLETION

1. corrective cost
2. specification
3. Benchmarking
4. tolerances
5. Statistical quality control
6. rework
7. acceptable quality levels
8. defect
9. Nondestructive testing
10. Quality

Part B: TRUE-FALSE

1. T
2. F
3. T
4. T
5. F
6. T
7. F
8. F
9. T
10. F

Part C: MULTIPLE CHOICE

1. b
2. c
3. d
4. d
5. a
6. d
7. b
8. c
9. b
10. c

CHAPTER 20

KEY TO CHAPTER 20 STUDY GUIDE

1. 2000
2. immigrant
3. jobs
4. twice
5. diversity
6. sexual orientation
7. correctness
8. performance
9. discriminate
10. 40
11. guidelines
12. employment
13. men
14. childbearing
15. bona fide occupational-qualification
16. disabled
17. affirmative action
18. Disparate
19. 15
20. life activities
21. disability
22. not
23. facilities
24. unpaid
25. must
26. dropouts
27. personal
28. Construct
29. advancement
30. pay
31. Comparable worth
32. proportion
33. supervised
34. Sexual harassment
35. investigation
36. power
37. victims
38. tolerate
39. report
40. suspicion
41. complain
42. changes
43. Praise
44. machines
45. conflicts
46. on file
47. telephone conversations
48. searches
49. Releasing
50. Lie detector
51. child care
52. employers
53. productive
54. facts

SELF-CHECK YOUR PROGRESS
Part A: COMPLETION

1. protected group
2. bona fide occupational qualification
3. Affirmative action
4. Differential treatment
5. Disparate effect
6. reverse discrimination
7. sexual harassment
8. Content validity
9. Construct validity
10. Comparable worth

Part B: TRUE-FALSE

| 1. T | 3. F | 5. T | 7. F | 9. T |
| 2. T | 4. F | 6. F | 8. T | 10. T |

Part C: MULTIPLE CHOICE

| 1. d | 3. d | 5. d | 7. c | 9. b |
| 2. a | 4. d | 6. b | 8. c | 10. c |

CHAPTER 21

KEY TO CHAPTER 21 STUDY GUIDE

1. Accidents
2. unsafe
3. $50 billion
4. killed
5. wrong
6. supervision
7. safety and health
8. inspections
9. citation
10. mandatory
11. inspection
12. posted
13. supervision
14. influential
15. accidents
16. new
17. suggestions
18. enforce
19. engineering
20. supervisor
21. protection
22. example
23. overestimate
24. Expect
25. hotel
26. electricity
27. One in 27
28. ergonomic
29. legs
30. used
31. loose
32. footwear
33. trained
34. reporting
35. fires
36. smoking
37. Evacuate
38. OSHA Form 200
39. dates
40. incident
41. medical care
42. workdays
43. minimize
44. done
45. $5,000
46. first aid
47. compliance
48. corrective
49. back care
50. popular

SELF-CHECK YOUR PROGRESS
Part A: COMPLETION

1. OSHA
2. incident rate
3. Williams-Steiger
4. hazard
5. Workers' compensation
6. severity rate
7. accident
8. Frequency rate
9. spontaneous combustion
10. engineer

Part B: TRUE-FALSE

| 1. F | 3. T | 5. T | 7. F | 9. T |
| 2. F | 4. T | 6. T | 8. T | 10. T |

Part C: MULTIPLE CHOICE

| 1. c | 3. c | 5. a | 7. c | 9. b |
| 2. c | 4. d | 6. b | 8. a | 10. b |

CHAPTER 22

KEY TO CHAPTER 22 STUDY GUIDE

1. accountable
2. unions
3. compulsory
4. responsibility
5. loyalty
6. National Labor Relations Act
7. difficult
8. improved
9. Threats
10. President of the United States
11. representation
12. federal court
13. forbidden
14. nonpayment
15. featherbedding
16. grievance
17. 60
18. sue
19. closed
20. union
21. Time-and-one-half
22. 40
23. collusion
24. consultants
25. 30 percent
26. one
27. rewards
28. support
29. union
30. bargaining
31. Interpretation
32. management
33. shop steward
34. grievances
35. 75 percent
36. arbitrator
37. contract
38. strikes

SELF-CHECK YOUR PROGRESS
Part A: COMPLETION

1. representation election
2. Collective bargaining
3. supervisors
4. Taft-Hartley Act
5. right-to-work laws
6. grievance procedure
7. arbitration
8. unfair labor practices
9. National Labor Relations Board (NLRB)
10. labor contract

Part B: TRUE-FALSE

1. T	3. T	5. F	7. T	9. T
2. F	4. F	6. T	8. F	10. T

Part C: MULTIPLE CHOICE

1. a	3. a	5. b	7. b	9. c
2. d	4. c	6. d	8. d	10. a

PERSONAL DEVELOPMENT PORTFOLIO

KEY TO PORTFOLIO STUDY GUIDE OUTLINES

1. career development
2. development
3. career path
4. weaknesses
5. targets and deadlines
6. in writing
7. Networking ("connection")
8. mentor
9. education
10. educational
11. supervisory development programs
12. aspirations
13. Time management
14. uncontrollable
15. 85 percent
16. specific
17. Routine
18. Creative
19. 20 percent
20. "A" tasks
21. limits
22. Interpersonal
23. unnecessary
24. Ambiguity
25. Inadequate resources
26. limitations
27. Break away
28. exercise
29. diversion
30. competence
31. gain access
32. use it
33. key person
34. win-lose
35. "negative"
36. challenging
37. salary goal
38. compromise

SELF-CHECK YOUR PROGRESS
Part A: COMPLETION

1. job competence
2. organization
3. leadership
4. stress
5. time budget
6. Prioritizing
7. ABC analysis
8. personal
9. vital few
10. burnout

Part B: TRUE-FALSE

1. F	3. T	5. T	7. T	9. T
2. T	4. T	6. F	8. F	10. F

Part C: MULTIPLE CHOICE

1. d	3. d	5. d	7. d	9. a
2. c	4. c	6. b	8. d	10. c